THE COMMONWEALTH AND INTERNATIONAL LIBRARY

MECHANICS OF MACHINES
VOLUME ONE

C0-AVT-887

MECHANICS OF MACHINES

VOLUME ONE

H. E. BARNACLE
B.Sc., A.M.I.Mech.E.

AND

G. E. WALKER
B.Sc., M.I.Mech.E.

PERGAMON PRESS

OXFORD · LONDON · EDINBURGH · NEW YORK
PARIS · FRANKFURT

PERGAMON PRESS LTD	Headington Hill Hall, Oxford 4 & 5 Fitzroy Square, London W.1
PERGAMON PRESS (SCOTLAND) LTD	2 & 3 Teviot Place, Edinburgh 1
PERGAMON PRESS INC.	122 East 55th Street, New York 22, N.Y.
GAUTHIER-VILLARS ED.	55 Quai des Grands-Augustins, Paris 6
PERGAMON PRESS G.m.b.H.	Kaiserstrasse 75, Frankfurt am Main
FEDERAL PUBLICATIONS LTD	Times House, River Valley Road, Singapore
SAMCAX BOOK SERVICES LTD	Queensway, P.O. Box 2720, Nairobi, Kenya

---

Set in 10 on 12 pt.   Printed in Great Britain
Times New Roman   by Page Bros., Norwich

CONTENTS

v

PREFACE

THESE two volumes on *Mechanics of Machines* are intended to cover the requirements of students of the subject beyond the standard of the Ordinary National Certificate or Diploma in Mechanical Engineering. Volume I is written with particular reference to the needs of the student attending a part-time course for the Higher National Certificate, although it is equally suitable for students in the earlier years of full-time or sandwich courses for the Higher National Diploma, the Diploma in Technology or the external degree of B.Sc. of London University.

An attempt has been made to treat the subject matter in a logical manner. The subject has been divided into three main sections, viz. kinematics in which motion only is dealt with, static forces including friction, and dynamic effects including elastic vibrations.

Volume II takes the subject to the stage necessary for students in the later years of Diploma and Degree courses. More advanced aspects and more complex problems on the subject matter of Volume I are dealt with and some more advanced topics are introduced.

The authors wish to express their thanks to the Senate of the University of London and to the Institution of Mechanical Engineers for permission to reproduce examination questions. Neither of these bodies is committed to approve the solutions or answers given.

INTRODUCTION

A MACHINE is essentially a device for the transmission of energy. Energy involves both force and movement and so the various elements of which a machine is composed will be subjected to forces and motions, the extent and nature of which are investigated and analysed in the subject of Mechanics of Machines.

The motion of a machine element may be linear (in a straight line) or angular (in a circle) or a combination of the two. The motion may be uniform or accelerated.

The force to which a machine element is subjected may be due to its own weight or the weight of other elements, externally applied forces, forces due to friction, or inertia effects caused by the acceleration and retardation of the machine elements.

The first three categories of forces are known as static forces and the last as dynamic forces.

Most of the quantities involved in the analysis of machines are vector quantities, i.e. they have magnitude, direction and sense, and can therefore be represented by vectors. It follows, therefore, that many of the problems can be more easily solved by graphical means than by calculation.

CHAPTER ONE

VELOCITY AND ACCELERATION IN LINK MECHANISMS

1.1. Absolute and Relative Velocity

The *absolute velocity* of a point is its velocity in relation to a fixed point which, in the context of our subject, will generally be any point on the rigid framework of a machine or mechanism.

The *relative velocity* of a point is its velocity relative to some other moving point.

If v_A = absolute velocity of a point A,

       v_{BA} = velocity of a point B relative to the point A,

       v_B = absolute velocity of the point B,

then v_B = vector sum of v_A and v_{BA}.

It follows that

    v_{BA} = vector difference of v_B and v_A.

This can be demonstrated graphically.

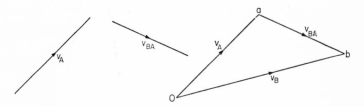

Fig. 1.1. Relative velocities

1

By choosing a suitable notation for the lettering of the vectors, the use of arrowheads may be eliminated.

Let the vector representing v_A be oa,

Let the vector representing v_B be ob,

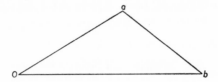

FIG. 1.2. Velocity vector diagram

then by drawing these two vectors from a common reference point O and joining ab, we see that the vector ab represents v_{BA}. It will be seen also that the vector ba represents v_{AB}. Note that the order in which the letters a and b are written indicates the sense of the vector.

1.2. Motion of a Rigid Link

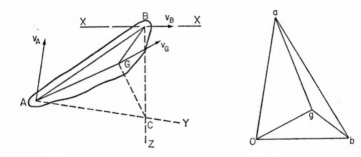

FIG. 1.3. Velocity diagram for a rigid link

The rigid link AB shown in Fig. 1.3 moves in the following manner:

   A has a known velocity v_A in the direction and sense shown by the arrow.

   B is constrained to move along the line XX.

It is required to make a complete investigation of the motion of the link.

   Using the notation and method given in section 1.1 the velocity diagram oab may be drawn in which

   oa represents v_A the absolute velocity of A,
   ob represents v_B the absolute velocity of B,
   ab represents v_{BA} the velocity of B relative to A.

If G is any other point on the link the velocity of G relative to A will be perpendicular to the line AG, and its velocity relative to B will be perpendicular to BG. These velocities will be represented in the velocity diagram by drawing lines from a and b in the above respective directions, the point of intersection being g. The line og will then represent the absolute velocity of G.

   If the point G lies on the line AB, the point g in the velocity diagram will lie on the line ab and will divide it in the same ratio as G divides AB.

1.3. Instantaneous or Virtual Centre

   It is rarely the case that a link in a mechanism moves in such a way that every point on the link continues to move with the same velocity in the same direction and sense. Any investigation such as that in section 1.2 applies only to the instant when the link is in the position shown. The velocities must therefore be looked upon as instantaneous values. If any point is rotating about some fixed point it is instantaneously moving in a direction perpendicular to the line joining the two points. Conversely, if a point is moving in a given direction it may be imagined to be instantaneously rotating about any other point in a line drawn perpendicular to its velocity.

Referring to Fig. 1.3, the point A may be imagined to be instantaneously rotating about any point in the line AY which is drawn perpendicular to v_A, and in the same way the point B may be imagined to be instantaneously rotating about any point in the line BZ which is drawn perpendicular to v_B. C, the point of intersection of AY and BZ is therefore a point about which both A and B may be imagined to be instantaneously rotating. The point C is known consequently as the instantaneous or virtual centre of rotation of A and B.

Now join the points GC and compare the two figures $AGBC$ and $agbo$. They will be seen to be similar, with each line of one figure perpendicular to the corresponding line in the other figure. Thus og, which represents the velocity of G, is perpendicular to CG, so that G also may be imagined as rotating instantaneously about C. C is therefore the instantaneous or virtual centre of the whole link.

Referring again to the two figures $AGBC$ and $agbo$, since they are similar, corresponding sides will be in the same ratio, i.e.

$$\frac{oa}{CA} = \frac{ob}{CB} = \frac{og}{CG} = \frac{ab}{AB} \text{ etc.}$$

or

$$\frac{v_A}{CA} = \frac{v_B}{CB} = \frac{v_G}{CG} = \frac{v_{BA}}{AB} \text{ etc.}$$

This gives us, therefore, a second method of investigating the motion of the link without the use of the vector diagram.

It should be noted also that the ratios (v_A/CA), (v_B/CB) and (v_G/CG) give the respective angular velocities about C of the points A, B and G and consequently the angular velocity of the complete link.

1.4. Velocity Diagrams for Link Mechanisms

The velocity diagram for a complete mechanism consisting of rigid links may be built up by drawing a velocity vector diagram for each link in turn.

Figure 1.4 shows a simple link mechanism in which O_1A is a crank rotating in a counterclockwise direction, AB is a connecting link which enables the crank to give to the link O_2B an oscillatory motion. O_1 and O_2 are fixed points.

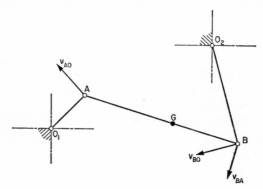

FIG. 1.4. Velocities in a four-bar chain

Let ω = angular velocity of the crank O_1A,

then $v_{AO} = \omega \cdot O_1A$ in the direction and sense shown,

v_{BO} (magnitude unknown) will be perpendicular to O_2B,

v_{BA} (magnitude unknown) will be perpendicular to AB.

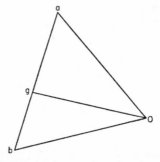

FIG. 1.5. Velocity diagram for a four-bar chain

The velocity diagram will therefore be obtained by drawing oa to represent the magnitude, direction and sense of v_A, and from o and a, lines perpendicular to O_2B and AB respectively, intersecting at b. The point g will lie on ab, dividing it in the same ratio as G divides AB. See Fig. 1.5.

From this diagram the magnitude and sense of each of the velocities v_B, v_{BA} and v_G may be found.

WORKED EXAMPLE.

1.1. In the mechanism shown in Fig. 1.6 the crank O_1A rotates in a counterclockwise direction at 60 rev/min. The triangular link ABD is connected by the connecting link DE to a slider E which moves in a horizontal path.

Determine, using (a) the method of virtual centres and (b) a velocity diagram, the velocity of the slider E and the angular velocity of the link ABD.

$O_1A = 8$ in., $AB = 28$ in., $AD = 25$ in., $BD = 7\frac{1}{2}$ in., $O_2B = 15$ in., $DE = 28$ in.

SOLUTION

$$v_{AO} = \frac{2\pi \times 8 \times 60}{60} = 50 \cdot 3 \text{ in/sec.}$$

(a) The instantaneous centre of the link ABD is given by the point of intersection of AO_1 produced and O_2B produced, as shown at C_1.

The instantaneous centre of the link DE is given by the point of intersection of DC_1 produced and a straight line from E perpendicular to the line of stroke of E, as shown at C_2.

From the diagram

$C_1A = 24$ in., $C_1D = 15$ in., $C_2D = 30 \cdot 9$ in., $C_2E = 24 \cdot 3$ in.,

therefore
$$\frac{v_{DO}}{C_1D} = \frac{v_{AO}}{C_1A},$$

$$v_{DO} = \frac{50 \cdot 3 \times 15}{24} = 31 \cdot 4 \text{ in/sec}$$

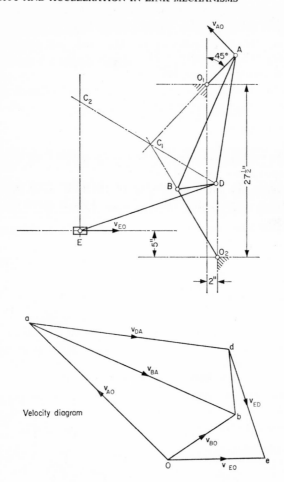

FIG. 1.6. Velocity diagram for a link mechanism

$$\frac{v_{EO}}{C_2E} = \frac{v_{DO}}{C_2D},$$

therefore

$$v_{EO} = \frac{24 \cdot 7 \times 31 \cdot 4}{30 \cdot 9} = 24 \cdot 7 \text{ in/sec,}$$

$$\omega_{ABD} = \frac{v_{AO}}{C_1 A} = \frac{50 \cdot 3}{24} = 2 \cdot 10 \text{ rad/sec.}$$

(b) The velocity diagram is drawn to a suitable scale as shown, and from it $v_{EO} = oe = 24 \cdot 7$ in/sec.

To obtain the angular velocity of the link ABD find from the velocity diagram the value of v_{DA}. This is given by $ad = 52 \cdot 5$ in/sec.

Then

$$\omega_{ABD} = \frac{v_{DA}}{AD} = \frac{52 \cdot 5}{25} = 2 \cdot 10 \text{ rad/sec.}$$

Note that triangle abd is geometrically similar to triangle ABD.

1.5 Acceleration of a Rigid Link

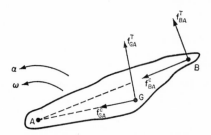

FIG. 1.7. Accelerations of a rigid link

The rigid link AB rotates about A with angular velocity ω and angular acceleration α, both counterclockwise.

Due to the angular velocity the point B will have a centripetal acceleration in the direction and sense from B to A, of magnitude $\omega^2 . AB$. In most practical problems this is more conveniently expressed in the form $\dfrac{v^2_{BA}}{AB}$. It will be represented by $f^C{}_{BA}$.

Due to the angular acceleration of the link, B will also have a tangential acceleration in a direction perpendicular to AB, of magnitude $\alpha . AB$. This acceleration will be represented by $f^T{}_{BA}$.

These two component accelerations, shown by arrows in Fig. 1.7 will combine to give a resultant acceleration whose value will be obtained by adding the two components vectorially.

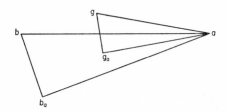

FIG. 1.8. Acceleration vector diagram for a rigid link

In the vector diagram of Fig. 1.8, $f^C{}_{BA}$ is represented in magnitude, direction and sense by the line ab_a and $f^T{}_{BA}$ is similarly represented by the line b_ab. The sum of the two vectors is ab and this line, therefore, represents in magnitude, direction and sense the resultant or total acceleration of B relative to A.

The point G will also have component accelerations relative to A.

$$f^C{}_{GA} = \frac{v_{GA}{}^2}{AG} \text{ in a direction and sense from } G \text{ to } A,$$

and

$$f^T{}_{GA} = \alpha . AG \text{ in a direction perpendicular to } AG.$$

The accelerations are shown by the vectors ag_a and g_ag respectively in Fig. 1.8 and it will be seen from considerations of geometrical similarity that the point g bears the same relation to a and b as G does to A and B. Thus the acceleration of any other point on a link may be determined in exactly the same manner as for the velocity.

Suppose the point A has itself centripetal and tangential accelerations relative to some fixed point O as shown by the vectors oa_o and a_oa respectively in Fig. 1.9, then the acceleration of B relative to O will be found by combining the two vector diagrams as shown. The resultant acceleration of B relative to O will then be represented by ob, and the resultant acceleration of G relative to O will be represented by og.

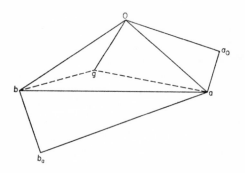

FIG. 1.9. Acceleration diagram

Acceleration Diagrams for Link Mechanisms

The acceleration diagram will be drawn for the mechanism shown in Fig. 1.4 for which the velocity diagram has already been drawn. It will be found to be of great help if all the component accelerations are listed, before starting to draw the acceleration diagram, indicating the lettering of the appropriate vector together with its direction and sense (if known). O_1A will be assumed to be rotating counterclockwise with uniform angular velocity ω. From the velocity diagram the velocities v_{BA} and v_{BO} will have been determined.

$$f^C{}_{AO} = \frac{v_{AO}{}^2}{OA}, \text{ represented by vector} \qquad oa \;\swarrow$$

$$f^T{}_{AO} = 0, \text{ (since angular velocity } \omega \text{ is constant)}$$

$$f^C{}_{BA} = \frac{v_{BA}{}^2}{AB}, \text{ represented by vector} \qquad ab_a \;\nwarrow$$

$$f^T{}_{BA} \text{ (unknown), represented by vector} \qquad b_a b \;\mid$$

$$f^C{}_{BO} = \frac{v_{BO}{}^2}{OB}, \text{ represented by vector} \qquad ob_o \;\nwarrow$$

$$f^T{}_{BO} \text{ (unknown), represented by vector} \qquad b_o b \;\diagup$$

The acceleration diagram can now be drawn by taking the vectors in the order given:

  oa which is known in magnitude, direction and sense,
  ab_a which is known in magnitude, direction and sense,
  $b_a b$ which is known in direction only,
  ob_o which is known in magnitude, direction and sense,
  $b_o b$ which is known in direction only.

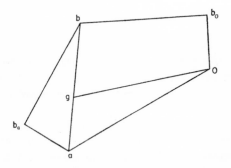

FIG. 1.10. Acceleration diagram for a four-bar chain

It will be seen from Fig. 1.10 that the two vectors, $b_a b$ and $b_o b$, which are known in direction only, intersect at the point b, thus completing the diagram. The point g is obtained by joining ab and dividing it at g in the same ratio as G divides AB.

From the diagram the magnitude and sense of the two tangential accelerations, $f^T{}_{BA}$ and $f^T{}_{BO}$, can be found. The vector og gives the total acceleration of G. If the angular acceleration of any link is required, this will be found by dividing the tangential acceleration of one end relative to the other by the length of the link, e.g.

$$a_{AB} = \frac{f^T{}_{BA}}{AB},$$

$$a_{O_2B} = \frac{f^T{}_{BO}}{O_2B}.$$

1.6. Sliding Acceleration

If any point in a mechanism is moving always in a straight line, e.g. the crosshead or piston of a reciprocating engine, it is clear that it cannot have a centripetal acceleration. It may be useful to consider the point as rotating in a circle of infinite radius in which case the centripetal acceleration v^2/r will be zero, and the tangential acceleration will be in a straight line. It is usually, in this case, called the sliding acceleration.

WORKED EXAMPLE

1.2. In the mechanism shown in Fig. 1.11 the sliders C and D move in straight paths as shown and are driven by the crank OA, through connecting links AC and BD. OA rotates in a clockwise direction at 60 rev/min and has an angular retardation of 8 rad/sec^2.

Determine for the position shown,
   (a) the velocity and acceleration of the slider D, and
   (b) the angular velocity and acceleration of the link BD.
        $OA = 2$ in., $AC = 6$ in., $AB = 2$ in., $BD = 9$ in.

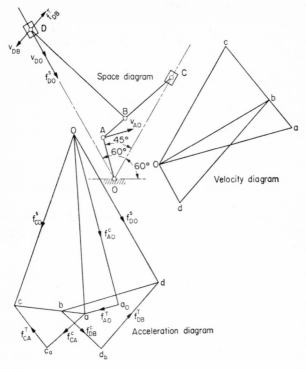

FIG. 1.11. Velocity and acceleration diagrams for a link mechanism

SOLUTION

$$v_{AO} = \frac{2\pi \times 3 \times 60}{60} = 18 \cdot 8 \text{ in/sec.}$$

The velocity diagram is drawn to a suitable scale and the following velocities obtained from it in order to calculate the values of centripetal acceleration:

$$v_{CA} = ac = 14 \cdot 2 \text{ in/sec,}$$

$$v_{DB} = bd = 18 \cdot 4 \text{ in/sec.}$$

Now making a list of accelerations:

$$f^C_{AO} = \frac{v_{AO}^2}{OA} = \frac{18 \cdot 8^2}{3} = 118 \text{ in/sec}^2 \quad oa_o \searrow,$$

$$f^T_{AO} = a.OA = 8 \times 3 = 24 \text{ in/sec}^2 \quad a_o a \nearrow,$$

$$f^C_{CA} = \frac{v_{CA}^2}{AC} = \frac{14 \cdot 2^2}{6} = 34 \text{ in/sec}^2 \quad ac_a \swarrow,$$

$$f^T_{CA} = \text{unknown} \qquad\qquad c_a c \searrow,$$

$$f^S_{CO} = \text{unknown} \qquad\qquad oc \nearrow.$$

From the above the point c will be located and the point b will be found by joining ac and dividing it at b such that $ab/ac = AB/AC$.

$$f^C_{DB} = \frac{v_{DB}^2}{BD} = \frac{18 \cdot 4^2}{9} = 38 \text{ in/sec}^2 \quad bd_b \searrow,$$

$$f^T_{DB} = \text{unknown} \qquad\qquad d_b d \nearrow,$$

$$f^S_{DO} = \text{unknown} \qquad\qquad od \searrow.$$

The point d is now located and the acceleration diagram completed.

From the velocity diagram

$$v_{DO} = od = \mathbf{5 \cdot 7 \text{ in/sec}},$$

$$\omega_{BD} = \frac{v_{DB}}{BD} = \frac{18 \cdot 4}{9} = \mathbf{2 \cdot 04 \text{ rad/sec}}.$$

Since v_{DB} acts to the left, the angular velocity of BD will be counterclockwise.

From the acceleration diagram

$$f^S{}_{DO} = od = \mathbf{115 \ in/sec^2}$$

in the same direction as the velocity.

The angular acceleration of BD is given by

$$a_{BD} = \frac{f^T{}_{DB}}{BD} = \frac{d_b d}{BD} = \frac{59}{9} = \mathbf{6 \cdot 56 \ rad/sec^2}.$$

Since $f^T{}_{DB}$ acts to the right, the angular acceleration of BD will be clockwise, i.e. opposite to the angular velocity. It is therefore a retardation.

1.7. Coriolis Acceleration

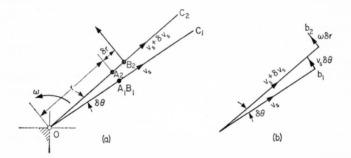

FIG. 1.12. Changes in velocity of a point sliding on a rotating link

Figure 1.12(a) shows a straight rigid link OC rotating in a counterclockwise direction with angular velocity ω. A is a point on the link and B is a point moving outwards along the link with a velocity v_s. Initially, B coincides with A as shown by A_1B_1. After a short increment of time δt, B will have moved a distance along the link δr to the point B_2 and the link will have rotated through an angle $\delta\theta$.

Consider the velocity of B relative to A. Initially, v_{BA} will be simply the sliding velocity v_s. Finally, however, in addition to the sliding velocity v_s, it will have a velocity relative to A, due to the rotation of the link, equal to $\omega\delta r$ in a direction perpendicular to the link which has now rotated to position 2. Figure 1.12(b) shows this change in relative velocity from ab_1 to ab_2 and it will be seen that the change in velocity of B relative to A is equal to $v_s\delta\theta + \omega\delta r$. If $\delta\theta$ is very small these two quantities may be considered to be in a straight line. Since this change takes place in time δt, the rate of change will be $(v_s\delta\theta + \omega\delta r)/\delta t$ and, as $\delta t \to 0$, will become

$$\frac{v_s \mathrm{d}\theta + \omega \mathrm{d}r}{\mathrm{d}t} = v_s \frac{\mathrm{d}\theta}{\mathrm{d}t} + \omega \frac{\mathrm{d}r}{\mathrm{d}t}.$$

But $\mathrm{d}\theta/\mathrm{d}t = \omega$ and $\mathrm{d}r/\mathrm{d}t = v_s$, therefore the rate of change of velocity of B relative to $A = 2\omega v_s$. This is called the Coriolis acceleration of B relative to A and is denoted by $f^{CC}{}_{BA}$. Its direction and sense should be noted in relation to ω and v_s.

It will be seen that f^{CC} is the product of two vector quantities ω and v_s and if either of these is negative (i.e. of opposite sense) the product, and hence f^{CC}, will be negative (i.e. of opposite sense). If both ω and v_s are negative the product will be positive

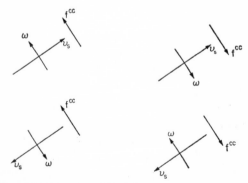

Fig. 1.13. Direction of Coriolis component acceleration

and hence the sense of f^{CC} will be the same as if both were positive. This is shown in Fig. 1.13.

A useful rule is that if the sliding velocity is radially outwards, the Coriolis acceleration will have the same sense as the tangential velocity of points on the rotating link, and vice versa.

It should be noted that B may also have, in addition, a sliding acceleration relative to A.

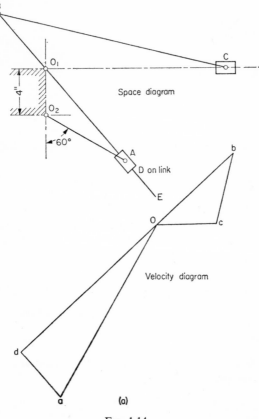

Fig. 1.14.

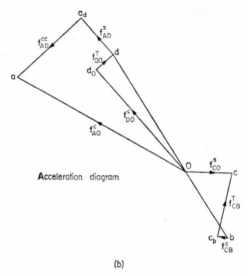

Acceleration diagram

(b)

FIG. 1.14. Velocity and acceleration diagrams for a quick-return mechanism

WORKED EXAMPLE

1.3. In the quick-return mechanism shown in Fig. 1.14, the crank O_2A rotates in a clockwise direction at a constant speed of 120 rev/min. The block A slides on the rotating link BO_1E which, in turn, drives the slider C through the connecting link BC.

Determine the velocity and acceleration of the slider C.

$$O_2A = 8 \text{ in.}, \quad O_1B = 6 \text{ in.}, \quad BC = 20 \text{ in.}$$

SOLUTION

D is a fixed point on the link BO_1E coincident with the point A in the configuration shown.

$$v_{AO} = \frac{2\pi \times 8 \times 120}{60} = 100 \text{ in/sec.}$$

The velocity diagram is drawn to scale and from it the following velocities are obtained:

$$v_{CO} = oc = \textbf{32 in/sec,}$$
$$v_{AD} = da = \textbf{33 in/sec,}$$
$$v_{DO} = od = \textbf{95 in/sec,}$$
$$v_{CB} = bc = \textbf{36 in/sec.}$$

Accelerations:

$$f^C{}_{AO} = \frac{v_{AO}^2}{O_2A} = \frac{100^2}{8} = 1250 \text{ in/sec}^2 \qquad oa \;\nwarrow$$

$$f^T{}_{AO} = 0,$$

$$f^C{}_{DO} = \frac{v_{DO}^2}{O_1D} = \frac{95^2}{10\cdot6} = 850 \text{ in/sec}^2 \qquad od_o \;\nwarrow$$

$$f^T{}_{DO} = \text{unknown} \qquad d_od \;\nearrow$$

$$f^{CC}{}_{AD} = 2_{O_1E} \times v_{AD} = 2 \times \frac{v_{DO}}{O_1D} \times v_{AD}$$

$$= 2 \times \frac{95}{10\cdot6} \times 33 = 590 \text{ in/sec}^2 \qquad a_da \;\swarrow$$

A is moving radially outwards along the link O_2E, therefore $f^{CC}{}_{AD}$ is in the same sense as v_{DO}.

$$f^S{}_{AD} = \text{unknown} \qquad da_d$$

The point d is now located. The point b is found by producing the line do and dividing it externally at b such that $ob/od = O_1B/O_1D$.

$$f^C{}_{CB} = \frac{v_{CB}^2}{BC} = \frac{36^2}{20} = 65 \text{ in/sec}^2 \qquad bc_b \;\leftarrow$$

$$f^T{}_{CB} = \text{unknown} \qquad c_bc \;/$$

$$f^S{}_{CO} = \text{unknown} \qquad oc \;-$$

The point c is now located and the acceleration diagram is complete.

From the acceleration diagram the acceleration of C is given by

$$f^S{}_{CO} = oc = \textbf{260 in/sec}^2.$$

This is in the same sense as the velocity so that the slider is actually accelerating.

Examples

1.4. In the mechanism of Fig. 1.15 the crank OA rotates at a constant speed of 250 rev/min in a clockwise direction. The block B slides in a straight path inclined at 20° to the vertical. The slider D moves in a straight horizontal path. Determine the velocity and acceleration of the slider D.
Answer: 1·75 ft/sec to the right, 153 ft/sec² to the left.

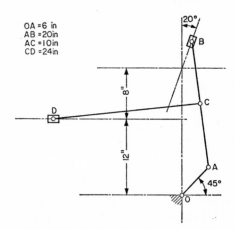

FIG. 1.15. Configuration for example 1.4

1.5. Figure 1.16 shows a mechanism in which the crank O_1A rotates uniformly in a clockwise direction at 12 rad/sec. Determine the velocity and acceleration of the slider D which moves in a horizontal path. Find also the angular velocity and angular acceleration of the link AB.
Answer: 10·4 in/sec to the left, 306 in/sec² to the left, 2·0 rad/sec clockwise, 6·2 rad/sec² counterclockwise.

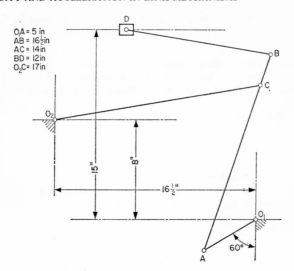

$O_1A = 5$ in
$AB = 16\frac{1}{2}$ in
$AC = 14$ in
$BD = 12$ in
$O_2C = 17$ in

FIG. 1.16. Configuration for example 1.5

1.6. In the radical valve gear shown in Fig. 1.17 the crank O_1A rotates uniformly in a clockwise direction at 100 rev/min. Determine the velocity and acceleration of the sliders B and F.

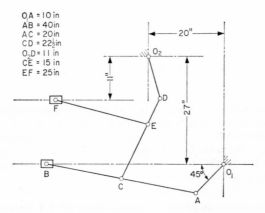

$O_1A = 10$ in
$AB = 40$ in
$AC = 20$ in
$CD = 22\frac{1}{2}$ in
$O_2D = 11$ in
$CE = 15$ in
$EF = 25$ in

FIG. 1.17. Configuration for example 1.6

B

Answer: 87 in/sec to the left, 780 in/sec² to the right, 35 in/sec to the left, 480 in/sec to the right.

1.7. In the shaping machine mechanism shown in Fig. 1.18 the crank O_1A rotates in a counterclockwise direction at a uniform speed of 60 rev/min. Determine, for the position shown, the velocity and acceleration of the tool holder C.

Answer: 23 in/sec to the left, 34 in/sec² to the left.

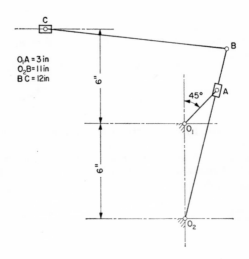

Fig. 1.18. Configuration for example 1.7

1.8. In the mechanism shown in Fig. 1.19, O_1ABO_2 is a four-bar chain. The link O_3D slides in a block which is pinned to the link AB at the point C. The crank O_1A rotates in a clockwise direction with uniform angular velocity of 10 rad/sec. Determine for the position shown, in which the points A, O_1 and O_2 are in a straight line, the angular acceleration of the link O_3D.

Answer: 20 rad/sec² counterclockwise.

1.9. In the reciprocating engine mechanism shown in Fig. 1.20 the oscillating link OD slides in a block pinned to the connecting rod at the point C. The

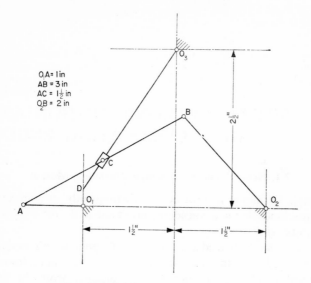

FIG. 1.19. Configuration for example 1.8

crank OA rotates in a clockwise direction at a uniform speed of 200 rev/min. Determine, for the position shown, the angular acceleration of the link OD. *Answer:* 11·9 rad/sec² counterclockwise.

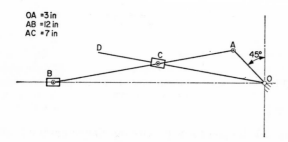

OA = 3 in
AB = 12 in
AC = 7 in

FIG. 1.20. Configuration for example 1.9

CHAPTER TWO

SIMPLE HARMONIC MOTION AND THE RECIPROCATING ENGINE

2.1. General Theory of Simple Harmonic Motion

Simple harmonic motion occurs so frequently in connection with machines that it is considered profitable to devote a separate section to its consideration.

It is commonly defined as the motion of a point which oscillates about a fixed point in such a manner that its acceleration towards the fixed point is proportional to its distance from the fixed point.

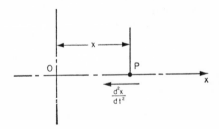

FIG. 2.1. Displacement and acceleration of a point P performing simple harmonic motion

In Fig. 2.1 the point P is performing simple harmonic motion about the point O. In the position shown, the displacement of P from O is x (measured to the right). The acceleration of P,

24

d^2x/dt^2 is towards O (i.e. to the left) and is therefore negative. From the definition its numerical value is proportional to x. The motion of P may therefore be represented by the equation

$$\frac{d^2x}{dt^2} \propto - x$$

or

$$\frac{d^2x}{dt^2} = - \text{ constant} \times x.$$

For reasons which will be shown below this constant will be written as n^2, giving

$$\frac{d^2x}{dt^2} + n^2x = 0. \tag{2.1}$$

A convenient way of visualising simple harmonic motion is shown in Fig. 2.2.

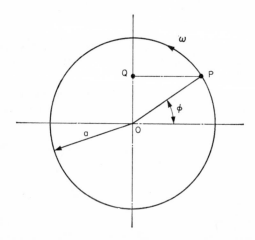

Fig. 2.2. As the point P rotates with uniform angular velocity its projection Q performs simple harmonic motion

The point P rotates in a counterclockwise direction round the circumference of a circle of radius a with uniform angular velocity ω. Q is the projection of P on the vertical diameter of the circle.

P will have a centripetal acceleration towards O, the centre of the circle, equal to $\omega^2 a$. The acceleration of Q will be the component of $\omega^2 a$ in a vertical direction, i.e. $\omega^2 a \sin \phi$, towards O. The displacement of Q from O is $r \sin \phi$. Thus it will be seen that Q performs simple harmonic motion about O.

Let $x =$ displacement of Q from O, then

$$x = a \sin \phi = a \sin \omega t. \qquad (2.2)$$

The velocity and acceleration of Q can be found by differentiating with respect to t, thus

$$\text{velocity} = \frac{\mathrm{d}x}{\mathrm{d}t} = \omega a \cos \omega t \qquad (2.3)$$

and

$$\text{acceleration} = \frac{\mathrm{d}^2 x}{\mathrm{d}t^2} = -\omega^2 a \sin \omega t. \qquad (2.4)$$

The amplitude of the motion is the maximum displacement from the centre of oscillation. This is equal to a, the radius of the circle in Fig. 2.2.

The periodic time or period of oscillation is the time taken to make one complete oscillation, which is the time taken for P to make one revolution, i.e.

$$T = \frac{2\pi}{\omega} \text{ sec.} \qquad (2.5)$$

The cyclical frequency is the number of complete oscillations performed per second, i.e.

$$f = \frac{\omega}{2\pi} \text{ cycles/sec.} \qquad (2.6)$$

In many problems involving simple harmonic motion it is convenient to work in terms of the value of ω which is known as the circular frequency.

The maximum velocity occurs when cos $\omega t = \pm 1$, and $= \pm \omega a$.

The maximum acceleration occurs when sin $\omega t = \pm 1$, and $= \pm \omega^2 a$.

2.2. Angular Simple Harmonic Motion

In the above analysis we have assumed that the motion of the point P is in a straight line. It may, however, move in the arc

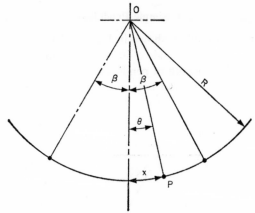

Fig. 2.3. Angular simple harmonic motion

of a circle as shown in Fig. 2.3 in which the amplitude of the motion is seen to be equal to $R\beta$.

Substituting this value for a in equation (2.1), we have

$$x = R\beta \sin \omega t. \tag{2.7}$$

Now divide by R and we have

$$\theta = \frac{x}{R} = \beta \sin \omega t. \tag{2.8}$$

Differentiating with respect to t we obtain

$$\frac{d\theta}{dt} = \omega\beta \cos \omega t, \qquad (2.9)$$

$$\frac{d^2\theta}{dt^2} = -\omega^2\beta \sin \omega t, \qquad (2.10)$$

giving the angular velocity and angular acceleration respectively of the line OP. The maximum values will be $\pm\omega\beta$ and $\pm\omega^2\beta$ respectively.

2.3. Simple Pendulum

In the simple pendulum shown in Fig. 2.4, let
$\quad \beta$ = amplitude of angular motion,
$\quad l$ = length of pendulum,
$\quad m$ = mass of bob.

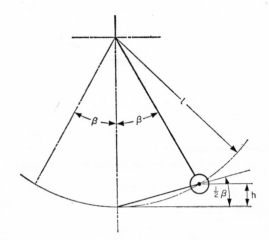

FIG. 2.4. Simple pendulum

In moving from the top of the swing to the lowest point where the bob will have its maximum velocity, the bob falls through a vertical height h.

$$\text{gain of K.E.} = \text{loss of P.E.}$$

$$\tfrac{1}{2}mv^2 = mgh = mg \,.\, 2l \sin^2 \tfrac{1}{2}\beta,$$

where v is the maximum velocity.

Therefore

$$v = 2 \sin \tfrac{1}{2}\beta \, \sqrt{gl}.$$

Maximum angular velocity $= v/l = 2 \sin \tfrac{1}{2}\beta \, \sqrt{(g/l)}$, thus

$$\omega\beta = 2 \sin \tfrac{1}{2}\beta \, \sqrt{\frac{g}{l}}.$$

If the angle of swing is small, then $\sin \tfrac{1}{2}\beta = \tfrac{1}{2}\beta$ and

$$\omega\beta = \beta \, \sqrt{\frac{g}{l}},$$

$$\omega = \sqrt{\frac{g}{l}}. \tag{2.11}$$

The period of oscillation is given by

$$T = \frac{2\pi}{\omega} = 2\pi \, \sqrt{\frac{l}{g}}. \tag{2.12}$$

2.4. Compound Pendulum

Figure 2.5 shows a body of mass m, having its centre of gravity at G, oscillating about the point O with angular amplitude of β. Let

l = distance of G from O,

k = radius of gyration about G.

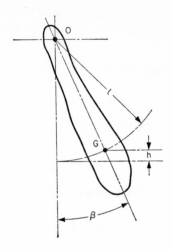

FIG. 2.5. Compound pendulum

As in section 2.3 the height of fall of the centre of gravity G will be given by

$$h = 2l \sin^2 \tfrac{1}{2}\beta$$

and loss of P.E. $= mg \cdot 2l \sin^2 \tfrac{1}{2}\beta$

gain in K.E. $= \tfrac{1}{2}$ moment of inertia $\times$ (angular velocity)^2

$$= \tfrac{1}{2} mk_o^2 \cdot (\omega\beta)^2,$$

where $k_o =$ radius of gyration about O

$$= \sqrt{(k^2 + l^2)}.$$

Therefore

$$\tfrac{1}{2}m (k^2 + l^2) (\beta)^2 = mg \cdot 2l \sin^2 \tfrac{1}{2}\beta,$$

and dividing each side by m,

$$\omega\beta = \sqrt{\left(\frac{gl}{k^2 + l^2}\right)} \cdot 2\sin\tfrac{1}{2}\beta.$$

Again, if β is small, $2\sin\tfrac{1}{2}\beta = \beta$

and

$$\omega = \sqrt{\left(\frac{gl}{k^2 + l^2}\right)} \tag{2.13}$$

and period of oscillation is given by

$$T = 2\pi\sqrt{\left(\frac{k^2 + l^2}{gl}\right)}. \tag{2.14}$$

The above method may be used to analyse any case of small oscillations under the action of gravity.

WORKED EXAMPLE

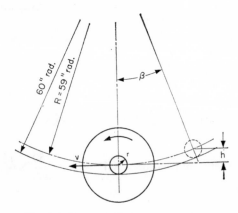

FIG. 2.6. Rotor oscillating on curved rails

2.1. A rotor which, with its shaft, has a mass of 30 lb and a moment of inertia of 150 lb. in², rests with its shaft on rails which have a radius of curvature of 60 in. as shown in Fig. 2.6. The diameter of the rotor shaft is 2 in. The rotor is displaced a small distance to one side of the equilibrium position and allowed to oscillate. Determine the period of oscillation.

SOLUTION.

Let β = angular amplitude of oscillation of centre of rotor shaft. Height of fall from top of swing,

$$h = 2R \sin^2 \tfrac{1}{2}\beta$$

$$= 118 \sin^2 \tfrac{1}{2}\beta \text{ in.}$$

Loss of P.E. $= 30 \times 118 \sin^2 \tfrac{1}{2}\beta$

$$= 3540 \sin^2 \tfrac{1}{2}\beta \text{ in/lb.}$$

The kinetic energy in the lowest position is made up of translational and rotational kinetic energy.

Let v = velocity of centre of rotor shaft in in/sec.

$$\text{Translational K.E.} = \tfrac{1}{2}mv^2 = \tfrac{1}{2} \times \frac{30}{386} v^2.$$

Angular velocity of rotor $= \dfrac{v}{r}$ rad/sec.

$$\text{Therefore rotational K.E.} = \tfrac{1}{2} \times \frac{150}{386} \times \frac{v^2}{l}.$$

Therefore

$$\left(\frac{15}{386} + \frac{75}{386}\right) v^2 = 3540 \sin^2 \tfrac{1}{2}\beta$$

$$v = \sin \tfrac{1}{2}\beta \sqrt{\left(\frac{3540 \times 386}{15 + 75}\right)}$$

$$\omega\beta = \frac{v}{R} = \frac{\sin \frac{1}{2}\beta}{59} \sqrt{\left(\frac{3540 \times 386}{90}\right)}$$

If β is small, $\sin \frac{1}{2}\beta = \frac{1}{2}\beta$.

Hence $\omega = \dfrac{1}{118} \sqrt{\left(\dfrac{3540 \times 386}{90}\right)}$

$\qquad = 1\cdot04$ rad/sec.

Period of oscillation $= \dfrac{2\pi}{\omega} = \dfrac{2\pi}{1\cdot04} = \mathbf{6\cdot05}$ **sec.**

2.5. The Reciprocating Engine

The motion of the piston or crosshead in a reciprocating engine may be considered as a modified simple harmonic motion.

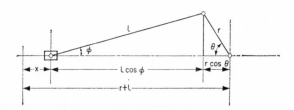

Fig. 2.7. Reciprocating engine mechanism

In the reciprocating engine mechanism shown in Fig. 2.7. the crank rotates clockwise with uniform angular velocity ω.

$\quad r$ = crank radius,

$\quad l$ = length of connecting rod,

$\quad x$ = displacement of piston from beginning of stroke.

$$x = l + r - r \cos \theta - l \cos \phi,$$

$$l \sin \phi = r \sin \phi,$$

$$\sin \phi = \frac{r}{l} \sin \phi,$$

$$\cos \phi = \sqrt{(1 - \sin^2 \phi)} = \sqrt{\left(1 - \frac{r^2}{l^2} \sin^2 \theta\right)},$$

hence

$$x = l + r - r \cos \theta - l \left(1 - \frac{r^2}{l^2} \sin^2 \theta\right)^{\frac{1}{2}}.$$

The value of r/l is usually in the region of $\frac{1}{4}$, in which case the term $r^2/l^2 \sin^2 \theta$ will never be greater than about $\frac{1}{16}$. We may therefore, with very little error, expand the bracketed quantity by the binomial theorem and neglect all but the first two terms.

Thus

$$x = l + r - r \cos \theta - l \left(1 - \frac{r^2}{2l^2} \sin^2 \theta + \dots\right).$$

Differentiating with respect to t we have

$$\frac{\mathrm{d}x}{\mathrm{d}t} = \left(r \sin \theta + \frac{r^2}{l} \sin \theta \cos \theta + \dots\right) \frac{\mathrm{d}\theta}{\mathrm{d}t}$$

$$= \omega r \left(\sin \theta + \frac{r}{2l} \sin 2\theta + \dots\right), \qquad (2.15)$$

$$\frac{\mathrm{d}^2 x}{\mathrm{d}t^2} = r \left(\cos \theta + \frac{r}{l} \cos 2\theta + \dots\right) \frac{\mathrm{d}\theta}{\mathrm{d}t}$$

$$= \omega^2 r \left(\cos \theta + \frac{r}{l} \cos 2\theta + \dots\right). \qquad (2.16)$$

It will be seen that if the first term only of the expressions for velocity and acceleration of the piston are used we have simple harmonic motion. The extent to which the motion is modified by the inclusion of the second term depends upon the value of r/l.

This effect is illustrated in Fig. 2.8 by graphs of velocity and acceleration of piston against crank angle.

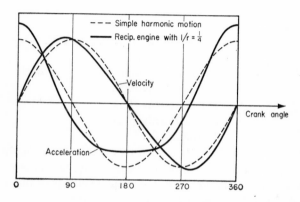

FIG. 2.8. Velocity and acceleration of piston of reciprocating engine

2.6. Graphical Determination of Piston Acceleration

Klein's Construction

In cases where it is required to determine the acceleration of the piston of a reciprocating engine for a number of crank positions, the following graphical method is considerably simpler and quicker than the normal method of drawing velocity and acceleration diagrams.

In Fig. 2.9 *OA* represents the crank and *AB* the connecting rod. Produce the connecting rod to cut a perpendicular to the line of stroke through the centre of the crankshaft at *C*.

With centre *A* and radius *AC* draw a circle; with *BA* as diameter draw another circle. Draw the common chord to these circles cutting *BA* at *D*, and the line of stroke at *E*.

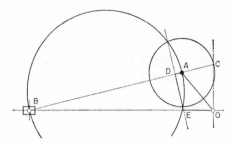

Fig. 2.9. Klein's construction for acceleration of piston

The figure $OADE$ is the acceleration diagram in which

$\qquad AO$ represents f^C_{AO},

$\qquad DA$ represents f^C_{BA},

$\qquad ED$ represents f^T_{BA},

$\qquad EO$ represents f^S_{BO}.

The scale of the diagram is such that if the above lengths are measured to the scale to which the engine mechanism is drawn, and multiplied by the square of the angular velocity of the crank, the actual values of the accelerations are given.

Examples

2.2. Determine the maximum velocity and acceleration of a point which performs simple harmonic motion with an amplitude of $\frac{1}{16}$ in. and a frequency of 50 c/s.

Answer: 19·6 in/sec, 6160 in/sec².

2.3. A simple pendulum of length 12 in. has a total angle of swing of 5°. Calculate the periodic time and the maximum angular velocity and acceleration.

Answer: 1·11 sec, 0·248 rad/sec, 1·33 rad/sec².

2.4. A connecting rod is suspended with the inner surface of the small-end bearing resting on a knife edge, and is allowed to swing as a pendulum. It is found to make 50 complete swings in 62 sec. The centre of gravity of the rod is 10 in. from the centre of the small-end bearing which is of $1\frac{1}{2}$ in. diameter.

Find the radius of gyration of the rod about an axis through the centre of gravity perpendicular to the plane of swing.

Answer: 6·78 in.

2.5. A flywheel is suspended by resting the inside of the rim on a horizontal knife-edge so that the wheel can swing in a vertical plane. The flywheel weighs 760 lb. The knife-edge is parallel to and 14 in. from the axis of the wheel. The time for making 1 small oscillation is 1·77 sec.

Assuming that the centre of gravity is in the axis of the wheel, find the radius of gyration about this axis.

Also find the torque to increase the speed of the wheel at a uniform rate from 240 to 250 rev/min in ¾ sec when the wheel is revolving about its axis.

Answer: 15·2 in., 640 lb in.   (L.U. 1951)

2.6. A flywheel weighing 10 lb is supported in bearings so that it can rotate about its axis. It is found to be out of balance and if displaced slightly from the equilibrium position and released it oscillates with a periodic time of 5·07 sec. A one-ounce weight is attached to the rim at a radius of 6 in. and vertically below the axis when the wheel is in equilibrium. It is now found to oscillate with a periodic time of 4·33 sec.

Determine the distance of the centre of gravity of the wheel from the axis of rotation and the radius of gyration of the wheel.

Answer: 0·101 in., 5·05 in.

CHAPTER THREE

CAMS

3.1. Introduction

Cams are used to convert continuous rotary motion into discontinuous reciprocating or oscillating motion. They may be of the plate or disc type imparting to the follower a specific reciprocating motion by virtue of the profile of the edge, or they may be of the cylindrical type in which the follower moves in a groove cut round the surface of a cylinder and of such a shape as to give the desired follower motion.

Owing to the acceleration and retardation of the follower it is generally necessary to provide an external force (usually a spring) to keep the follower in contact with the cam profile. In order to provide the correct spring force it is necessary, therefore, to determine the acceleration and retardation of the follower.

Cam profiles may be designed either (a) to give a specified type of motion to the follower (e.g. uniform acceleration or S.H.M.) or (b) to have simple geometrical profiles consisting of circular arcs and straight lines. In case (a) the whole of the motion of the follower may be analysed mathematically. In (b), however, a graphical method must be used to obtain a displacement time graph which can then be differentiated either graphically or numerically, or if isolated values only are required an equivalent link mechanism may be derived and velocity and acceleration diagrams drawn.

3.2. Cams for which the Follower Motion is Specified

(a) *Uniform Acceleration and Retardation*

Figure 3.1 shows a graph of displacement of follower against rotation of cam together with the derived graphs of velocity and acceleration. This shows that the follower moves with uniform acceleration through a distance x_1 in., whilst the cam rotates through an angle θ_1 degrees, and with uniform retardation through a distance x_2 in., whilst the cam rotates through an angle θ_2 degrees.

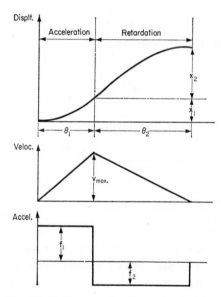

Fig. 3.1. Uniform acceleration and retardation

Let ω = uniform angular velocity of cam in rad/sec, and time taken for cam rotation of θ_1 degrees

$$t_1 = \theta_1 \times \frac{\pi}{180} \times \frac{1}{\omega} = \frac{\pi}{180\omega} \cdot \theta_1 \text{ sec.}$$

Thus for acceleration period,

$$\text{average velocity} = \frac{x_1}{t_1} \text{ in/sec,}$$

maximum velocity

$$v_{\max} = \frac{2x_1}{t_1} = 2\left(\frac{180\omega}{\pi}\right)\frac{x_1}{\theta_1} \text{ in/sec,} \tag{3.1}$$

acceleration

$$f_1 = \frac{v_{\max}}{t_1} = \frac{2x_1}{t_1{}^2} = \left(\frac{180\omega}{\pi}\right)^2 \frac{x_1}{\theta_1{}^2} \text{ in/sec}^2. \tag{3.2}$$

Similarly, for the retardation period,

$$t_2 = \frac{\pi}{180\omega} \cdot \theta_2 \text{ sec,}$$

maximum velocity

$$= \frac{2x_2}{t_2} = 2\left(\frac{180\omega}{\pi}\right)\frac{x_2}{\theta_2} \text{ in/sec,} \tag{3.3}$$

retardation

$$f_2 = \frac{2x_2}{t_2{}^2} = 2\left(\frac{180\omega}{\pi}\right)^2 \frac{x_2}{\theta_2{}^2} \text{ in/sec}^2. \tag{3.4}$$

It should be noted that if there is to be a smooth transition from the acceleration period to the retardation period, $v_{\max}$ must have the same value for both, i.e.

$$2\left(\frac{180\omega}{\pi}\right)\frac{x_1}{\theta_1} = 2\left(\frac{180\omega}{\pi}\right)\frac{x_2}{\theta_2}$$

or

$$\frac{x_1}{x_2} = \frac{\theta_1}{\theta_2}.$$

(b) Simple Harmonic Motion

Figure 3.2 shows graphs of displacement, velocity and acceleration for simple harmonic motion of the follower. The motion is that of the point Q, the projection on the diameter of the point P which rotates with uniform angular velocity round the circumference of a circle of radius a. P rotates through π radians whilst the cam rotates through θ degrees.

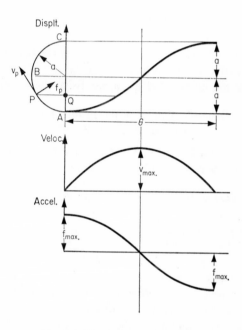

FIG. 3.2. Simple harmonic motion

Thus if ω = uniform angular velocity of the cam in rad/sec, the angular velocity of P will be given by

$$\omega \times \frac{\pi}{(\pi/180) \cdot \theta} = \frac{180\omega}{\theta}.$$

The maximum velocity of Q occurs when P is at the point B on the circle and is equal to the peripheral velocity of P, i.e.

$$v_{max} = \frac{180\omega}{\theta} \cdot a. \tag{3.5}$$

The maximum acceleration of Q occurs when P is at the points A and C on the circle and is equal to the centripetal acceleration of P, i.e.

$$f_{max} = \left(\frac{180\omega}{\theta}\right)^2 a. \tag{3.6}$$

This will be positive when P is at A, i.e. at the beginning of the lift, and negative when P is at C, i.e. at the end of the lift.

Note that the lift is equal to $2a$, i.e. twice the amplitude.

3.3. Determination of Cam Profile for a given Motion of the Follower

It will be assumed in the first instance that the follower consists of a roller whose centre performs the desired motion.

(a) Line of action of follower passing through centre of rotation of cam

Figure 3.3 shows the method of constructing the required cam profile. The graph of displacement of the follower against angular rotation of the cam is drawn and verticals are erected at equal intervals $\delta\theta$. The points of intersection of these verticals with the displacement graph are projected horizontally on to a vertical OS through the centre of rotation of the cam. Radial lines are now drawn from the centre of rotation of the cam at equal intervals $\delta\theta$ corresponding to the verticals on the displacement graph. The points on the vertical OS are now projected by arcs of circles with centre O on to the corresponding radials, thus giving the locus of the centre of the follower relative to the centre of rotation of the cam. Circles of radius equal to that of the roller are now drawn at the respective roller centres and the cam profile is drawn tangentially to these circles.

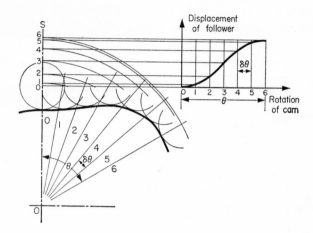

FIG. 3.3. Determination of cam profile—line of stroke of follower passes through centre of rotation of cam

(b) *Line of action of follower offset from centre of rotation of cam*

Figure 3.4 shows that the method is precisely the same as in the previous cases except that the radial lines from the centre of rotation of the cam are replaced by lines drawn tangentially to a circle of radius equal to the amount by which the line of action of the follower is offset from the centre of rotation of the cam.

3.4. Followers of Types other than Roller

(a) *Spherical-ended follower*. The method used for this type is exactly the same as that for a roller.

(b) *Flat-footed follower*. The method is the same as for the roller type up to the point where the locus of the centre of roller follower is obtained. Straight lines are now drawn through the respective roller centres as shown in Fig. 3.5. The cam profile is now drawn tangentially to these lines.

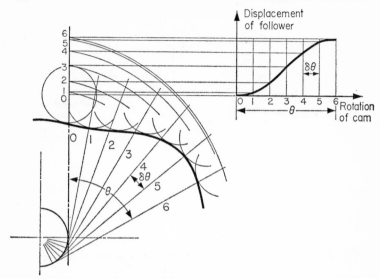

FIG. 3.4. Determination of cam profile—line of stroke of follower
offset from centre of rotation of cam

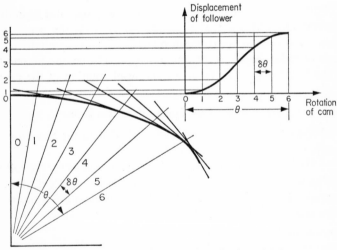

FIG. 3.5. Determination of cam profile—flat-footed follower

3.5. Follower on Oscillating Link

In this type of mechanism the follower moves in the arc of a circle and the construction described in sections 3.3 and 3.4 will be modified as shown in Fig. 3.6.

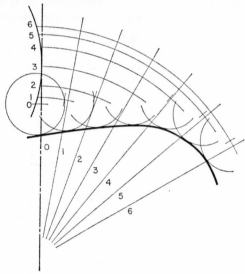

Fig. 3.6. Determination of cam profile—rocking follower

The centre of the follower corresponding to each radial is offset from the radial by the amount by which the path of the follower deviates from a straight line.

3.6. Determination of Motion of Follower for a given Cam Profile

A graph of displacement of the follower against the rotation of the cam may be constructed by following exactly the reverse procedure to that used in determining the cam profile for a given follower motion. The following example illustrates the method used.

Having obtained the graph of displacement of the follower, the method of graphical differentiation can be used to obtain curves of velocity and acceleration.

WORKED EXAMPLE

3.1. The cam shown in Fig. 3.7 rotates about O at a uniform speed of 500 rev/min and operates a follower attached to the roller of centre Q; the path of Q is a straight line passing through O.

Draw the time–lift diagram for the roller centre Q, on a base of

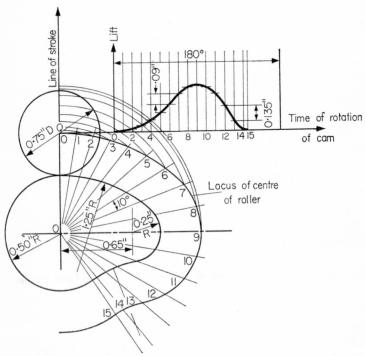

FIG. 3.7. Determination of motion of follower for a given cam profile

1 in. to 0·01 sec and to a vertical scale of four times full size, for a movement of 180° from the position shown. Determine the maximum velocity of the roller centre Q and the cam angle at which it occurs.

SOLUTION

The locus of the roller centre is drawn and radial lines from the centre of rotation O are drawn for every 10° of cam rotation. The points of intersection of these radial lines with the locus of the roller centre are then projected by circular arcs on to the line of stroke. These points are then projected horizontally to cut the corresponding verticals in the time–lift diagram,

$$\text{Speed of rotation of cam} = 500 \text{ rev/min,}$$

therefore angular rotation in 0·01 sec $= \dfrac{500 \times 360}{60 \times 100} = 30°$.

The horizontal scale is thus 1 in. $= 30°$ and the verticals will be spaced $\frac{1}{3}$ in. apart.

Maximum upward velocity occurs between positions 6 and 7, i.e. when the cam has rotated through, say, 65° and will be equal to

$$\frac{0·09}{0·0033} = 27 \text{ in/sec.}$$

Maximum downward velocity occurs between positions 12 and 13, i.e. when the cam has rotated through, say, 125° and will be equal to

$$\frac{0·135}{0·0033} = 40·5 \text{ in/sec.}$$

3.7. Equivalent Link Mechanism

Where accurate values of the velocity and acceleration of the follower are required for isolated positions of a cam, whose profile is made up of circular arcs and straight lines, an equivalent link mechanism can be derived and velocity and acceleration diagrams can be drawn as described in Chapter 1.

(a) Circular arc cam with roller follower

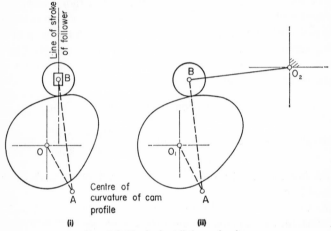

Fig. 3.8. Equivalent link mechanism

In Fig. 3.8 are shown cases of a circular arc cam with a roller follower which (i) moves in a straight path and (ii) is carried by an oscillating link. In both cases A is the centre of curvature of the cam profile at the point of contact with the roller, and B is the centre of the roller. It will be seen that for all points on the cam profile for which the centre of curvature is A, the distance AB will be constant and the cam and roller may be replaced by a straight rigid link AB. The point A rotates about O with the same angular velocity as the cam which may, therefore, be replaced by a crank OA. It is clear, therefore, that the cam and roller may be replaced in (i) by a slider–crank mechanism and (ii) by a four-bar chain.

When the roller is in contact with the nose of the cam which has a different radius of curvature from the flank, the centre of curvature will be different as shown by A' in Fig. 3.9 and the equivalent crank will be OA' and the equivalent connecting rod $A'B$.

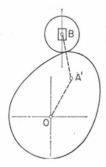

Fig. 3.9. Equivalent link mechanism

(b) Tangent cam with roller follower

Figure 3.10 shows the circular arc cam of the previous cases replaced by a tangent or straight-sided cam. It will be seen that

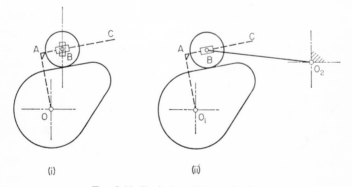

Fig. 3.10. Equivalent link mechanism

the centre of the roller B moves, relatively to the cam, in a straight line parallel to the flank of the cam. It may therefore be imagined as sliding along a straight link AC which rotates about O, with the same angular velocity as the cam.

The equivalent link mechanism for case (i) consists, therefore, of a right-angled crank OAC on the portion AC of which slides a block pinjointed to a second block which slides along the line of stroke of the follower. In case (ii) there is a single sliding block which is pinjointed to the end of the oscillating link BC.

Equivalent link mechanisms may be derived in the same way for cases where other types of follower are used.

3.8. Analytical Method of Determining Velocity and Acceleration of Follower

This method can be applied to circular-arc or straight-sided cams and by its means expressions for velocity and acceleration of the follower will be obtained which apply over a given range of cam rotation. The method consists in obtaining a trigonometrical relationship between the displacement of the follower and the angle of rotation of the cam and differentiating the expression

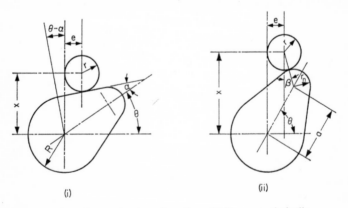

(i)   (ii)

Fig. 3.11. Determination of motion of follower analytically

for displacement twice successively with respect to time. The case will be considered of a tangent cam with a roller follower whose line of stroke is a straight line.

(a) *Roller in contact with flank of cam*

Referring to Fig. 3.11 (i),

R = base radius of cam,

r = radius of roller,

e = distance of line of stroke from centre of rotation of cam,

a = angle between flank and centre line of cam,

θ = angular rotation of cam,

x = distance of centre of follower from centre of rotation of cam measured parallel to line of stroke.

Then

$$x = (R + r) \sec (\theta - a) + e \tan (\theta - a), \qquad (3.7)$$

$$\frac{\mathrm{d}x}{\mathrm{d}t} = \left\{ \frac{(R + r) \sin (\theta - a)}{\cos^2 (\theta - a)} + e \sec^2 (\theta - a) \right\} \frac{\mathrm{d}\theta}{\mathrm{d}t}$$

$$= \frac{(R + r) \sin (\theta - a) + e}{\cos^2 (\theta - a)} \frac{\mathrm{d}\theta}{\mathrm{d}t}. \qquad (3.8)$$

If the cam rotates with uniform angular velocity then

$$\mathrm{d}\theta/\mathrm{d}t = \text{const.}$$

$$\frac{\mathrm{d}^2 x}{\mathrm{d}t^2} =$$

$$\frac{(R+r) \cos^3 (\theta - a) + 2 \{(R+r) \sin (\theta - a) + e\} \cos \theta \sin \theta}{\cos^4 (\theta - a)} \left(\frac{\mathrm{d}\theta}{\mathrm{d}t}\right)^2$$

$$= \frac{(R + r) \{1 + \sin^2 (\theta - a)\} + 2e \sin (\theta - a)}{\cos^3 (\theta - a)} \left(\frac{\mathrm{d}\theta}{\mathrm{d}t}\right)^2. \qquad (3.9)$$

These expressions for velocity and acceleration of the follower apply so long as the roller is in contact with the straight flank of the cam, i.e. until it reaches the point where the flank is tangential to the arc of the nose of the cam. An examination of the three expressions for displacement, velocity and acceleration shows that within the limits of contact with the flank all three increase as θ increases; thus for this portion of the stroke maximum velocity and acceleration occur at the point of transition from the flank to the nose. Beyond this point the expression for x will be different.

(b) *Roller in contact with nose of cam*

Referring to Fig. 3.11 (ii),

a = distance from centre of rotation to centre of nose radius,
r_n = radius of nose of cam.

Then
$$x = a \sin \theta + (r + r_n) \cos \beta.$$

Now
$$(r + r_n) \sin \beta = a \cos \theta - e$$

$$\sin \beta = \frac{a \cos \theta - e}{r + r_n}$$

$$\cos \beta = \sqrt{(1 - \sin^2 \beta)} = \sqrt{\left\{1 - \left(\frac{a \cos \theta - e}{r + r_n}\right)^2\right\}}.$$

Therefore
$$x = a \sin \theta + \{(r + r_n)^2 - (a \cos \theta - e)^2\}^{\frac{1}{2}}.$$

Let $r + r_n = b$, then
$$x = a \sin \theta + \{b^2 - (a \cos \theta - e)^2\}^{\frac{1}{2}}. \tag{3.10}$$

Assuming $\mathrm{d}\theta/\mathrm{d}t$ = constant, successive differentiation with respect to t gives

$$\frac{\mathrm{d}x}{\mathrm{d}t} = [a \cos \theta + \{b^2 - (a \cos \theta - e)^2\}^{-\frac{1}{2}} (\tfrac{1}{2}a^2 \sin 2\theta -$$

$$- ea \sin \theta)] \frac{\mathrm{d}\theta}{\mathrm{d}t}, \tag{3.11}$$

$$\frac{d^2x}{dt^2} = \left[- a \sin \theta + \frac{\{b^2 - (a \cos \theta - e)^2\} (a^2 \cos 2\theta - ea \cos \theta) - (\frac{1}{2}a^2 \sin 2\theta - ea \sin \theta)^2}{\{b^2 - (a \cos \theta - e)^2\}^{3/2}} \right].$$

(3.12)

The transition from the flank to the nose occurs when

$$a \cos \theta = e + (r + r_n) \sin (\theta - \alpha).$$

If the line of stroke of the follower passes through the centre of rotation of the cam, then $e = 0$ and the above expressions reduced to the following.

(a) *Roller in Contact with Flank of Cam*

$$x = (R + r) \sec (\theta - \alpha),$$

(3.13)

$$\frac{dx}{dt} = \frac{(R + r) \sin (\theta - \alpha)}{\cos^2 (\theta - \alpha)} \cdot \frac{d\theta}{dt},$$

(3.14)

$$\frac{d^2x}{dt^2} = \frac{(R + r) \{1 + \sin^2 (\theta - \alpha)\}}{\cos^3 (\theta - \alpha)} \cdot \left(\frac{d\theta}{dt}\right)^2.$$

(3.15)

(b) *Roller in Contact with Nose of Cam*

$$x = a \sin \theta + (b^2 - a^2 \cos^2 \theta)^{\frac{1}{2}},$$

(3.16)

$$\frac{dx}{dt} = [a \cos \theta + \tfrac{1}{2}a^2 \sin 2\theta (b^2 - a^2 \cos^2 \theta)^{-\frac{1}{2}}] \frac{d\theta}{dt},$$

(3.17)

$$\frac{d^2x}{dt^2} = \left[- a \sin \theta + \frac{a^2 \cos 2\theta (b^2 - a^2 \cos^2 \theta) - \tfrac{1}{4}a^4 \sin^2 2\theta}{(b^2 - a^2 \cos^2 \theta)^{3/2}} \right] \left(\frac{d\theta}{dt}\right)^2.$$

(3.18)

c

The transition from flank to nose will occur when

$$a \cos \theta = (r + r_n) \sin (\theta - a).$$

WORKED EXAMPLE

3.2. A symmetrical tangent cam has a base radius of 2 in. and a nose radius of $\frac{1}{2}$ in. The distance between the centre of rotation and the centre of the nose radius is 2 in. It operates a roller follower 2 in. in diameter whose centre moves in a straight path offset $\frac{1}{2}$ in. to the right of the centre of rotation of the cam. If the cam rotates in a counterclockwise direction at a constant speed of 500 rev/min, determine the acceleration of the follower just before and just after it passes from the flank to the nose on the upstroke.

SOLUTION

Referring to Fig. 3.11 and using the same notation,

$$\sin a = \frac{R - r_n}{a} = \frac{2 - 0 \cdot 5}{2} = 0 \cdot 75,$$

therefore

$$a = \mathbf{48 \cdot 6}^\circ.$$

The transition from flank to nose occurs when

$$a \cos \theta = e + (r + r_n) \sin (\theta - a),$$

$$2 \cos \theta = 0 \cdot 5 + 1 \cdot 5 \sin (\theta - 48 \cdot 6^\circ),$$

$$\text{i.e. } \theta = \mathbf{63 \cdot 6}^\circ.$$

(a) *Just Before Transition*

$$\frac{\mathrm{d}^2 x}{\mathrm{d} t^2} = \omega^2 \cdot \frac{(R + r) \{1 + \sin^2 (\theta - a)\} + 2e \sin (\theta - a)}{\cos^3 (\theta - a)}$$

$$= \frac{2\pi \times 500}{60} = 52 \cdot 3 \text{ rad/sec},$$

$$\frac{d^2x}{dt^2} = 52 \cdot 3^2 \times \frac{3\{1 + \sin^2 15°\} + \sin 15°}{\cos^3 15°}$$

$$= \frac{2750 \times (3 \cdot 20 + 0 \cdot 259)}{0 \cdot 900}$$

$$= \mathbf{10{,}560 \ in/sec^2.}$$

(b) *Just After Transition*

Substituting numerical values in eqn. (3.12) we have

$$\frac{d^2x}{dt^2} = 2750 \left[-1 \cdot 792 + \right.$$

$$\left. + \frac{\{2 \cdot 25 - (0 \cdot 890 - 0 \cdot 5)^2\}(-2 \cdot 420 - 0 \cdot 445) - (1 \cdot 594 - 0 \cdot 896)^2}{\{2 \cdot 25 - (0 \cdot 890 - 0 \cdot 5)^2\}^{3/2}} \right]$$

$$= \mathbf{-16{,}300 \ in/sec^2.}$$

The negative sign indicates that this is, in fact, retardation.

Examples

3.3. A cam operates a flat or palm follower. The follower moves in a straight line which is normal to its working face. The profile of the cam is formed by a base circle of 3 in. diameter joined by two tangents to a nose of $\frac{3}{4}$ in. radius. The lift of the follower is 1 in., and the speed of the cam is 300 rev/min about an axis which contains the centre of the base circle. Draw the displacement–time and velocity–time curves for the period of lifting only.

(L.U. 1944)

3.4. The profile of a cam is a circle of 4 in. diameter, and the cam rotates about an axis which is $\frac{7}{8}$ in. from the centre of the circle. The cam operates a roller-ended follower, which moves in a straight line passing $\frac{5}{8}$ in. to one side of the axis of revolution, the roller diameter being $2\frac{1}{2}$ in.

Draw a curve showing the follower lift full size on a base of 1 in. to 40 for one complete revolution.

(L.U. 1948)

3.5. The lift diagram for a follower operated by a cam is shown in Fig. 3.12; the follower is at rest for the remaining 210° of revolution. The follower moves in a straight line passing through the axis of rotation of the cam, and carries a roller $1\frac{3}{4}$ in. diameter, the minimum radius of the cam being $2\frac{3}{4}$ in.

Draw the cam profile, full size, leaving sufficient construction line to indicate clearly the method used.

(L.U. 1949)

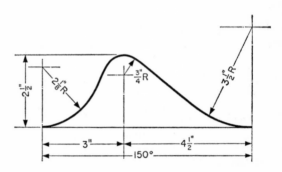

Fig. 3.12. Lift diagram for example 3.5

3.6. A valve is required to lift $1\frac{3}{4}$ in. with equal uniform acceleration and retardation. The tappet which operates the valve is provided with a roller of 2 in. diameter and its line of stroke intersects the axis of the cam at right angles. The cam turns through 60° during each stroke of the tappet and the shortest distance between the axes of the roller and the cam is 3 in. Draw one half the outline of the cam.

If the cam turns at a uniform speed of 210 rev/min, find the acceleration and the maximum velocity of the valve.

Answer: 3090 in/sec², 73·5 in/sec.   (I.Mech.E. 1948)

3.7. A cam turns at a uniform speed of 180 rev/min and gives an oscillating follower, $2\frac{1}{2}$ in. long, an angular displacement of 30° on each stroke. The follower is fitted with a roller, 2 in. diameter, which makes contact with the profile of the cam. The outward and return displacements each take place with uniform acceleration and retardation while the cam turns through 60° and there is a period of dwell in the outward position while the cam turns through 15°.

If the axis of the follower is $3\frac{1}{2}$ in. from the axis of the cam, and the least distance of the roller axis from the cam axis is $2\frac{1}{2}$ in., draw the outline of the cam.

Find the maximum angular velocity and the angular acceleration of the follower.

Answer: 18·8 rad/sec, 676 rad/sec². (I.Mech.E. 1949)

3.8. A cam turns with constant speed about a centre on the axis of the follower. The follower is lifted 1 in. during a rotation of 90° of the cam, the motion being simple harmonic. Draw the lift–angular displacement curve for this interval. If the follower is flat faced and the cam profile has a minimum radius of 1·25 in., draw the lifting portion of the cam profile.

If the cam speed is 2 rev/sec find the maximum velocity and acceleration of the follower.

Answer: 12·6 in/sec, 316 in/sec². (I.Mech.E. 1953)

3.9. A symmetrical tangent cam has a minimum radius of 1 in., and gives to a roller follower a lift of $\frac{1}{2}$ in. The nose radius of the cam is $\frac{1}{2}$ in. and the diameter of the follower is 1 in. The path of the follower is a straight line passing through the axis of the cam.

If the cam rotates uniformly at 250 rev/min calculate the velocity and acceleration of the follower (*a*) at the beginning of lift and (b) just before it leaves the straight flank of the cam.

Answer: (a) 0, 1030 in/sec²; (b) 26·2 in/sec; 1980 in/sec².

3.10. Making use of an equivalent link mechanism for the cam and follower of worked example 2.1, determine the velocity of the follower as it passes from the flank radius to the nose radius on the upstroke, and the acceleration of the follower just before and just after this instant.

Answer: 28·7 in/sec, 1490 in/sec², −3400 in/sec².

CHAPTER FOUR

TOOTHED GEARING

4.1. Gear Tooth Profiles

Various geometrical curves have been used in the past for the profile of gear teeth but for some time now the involute form has been adopted to the almost complete exclusion of any other shape. For this reason only the involute profile will be dealt with here and before proceeding to the consideration of gear teeth it will be advisable to investigate a certain property of the involute.

The involute is the locus of a point on a straight line which rolls without slipping round the circumference of a circle called the base circle.

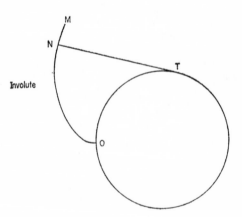

FIG. 4.1. Property of the involute

In Fig. 4.1 the curve OM is the involute traced out by the point N on the straight line TN. It is clear that as the line rolls round the circle the point of contact T will be the instantaneous centre of rotation of the line TN. The path of N is, therefore, perpendicular to the line TN. This condition may be expressed in the following way: the normal to an involute at any point is tangential to the base circle.

4.2. Condition for Uniform Velocity Ratio

If the velocity ratio of two gear wheels is to be uniform their relative motion must be the same as that of two friction discs having diameters equal to the respective pitch circle diameters of the wheels. The instantaneous relative motion is thus one of rotation about the point of contact of the pitch circles, called the pitch point. In other words, the pitch point is the instantaneous centre of relative rotation of the two wheels. Consider two wheels A and B rotating in gear with uniform velocity ratio. Then, if the above condition is to hold, any point C on wheel A which is in contact with a point D on wheel B must be moving, relative to D, in a direction perpendicular to a line joining it to the pitch point P and vice versa. Two such points will occur at the point of contact of two teeth on the respective wheels. This condition is shown in Fig. 4.2.

C is a point on a tooth profile of wheel A in contact with the point D on a tooth profile of wheel B. P is the pitch point through which passes the line EF which is perpendicular to the relative velocities v_{CD} and v_{DC}. For this motion to be possible the tooth profiles must be tangential to v_{CD} and v_{DC}. From the property of the involute, stated in paragraph 41, it will be seen that if CE and DF are respectively tangential to the base circles A and B and the tooth profiles are involutes drawn to these base circles the required condition will be obtained.

If friction at the point of contact is neglected, then the thrust between the two teeth will act in the direction of the line EF, the common tangent to the base circles, so that this line is both

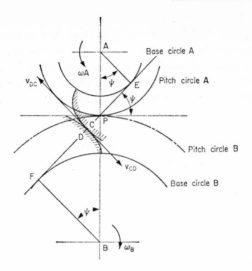

Fig. 4.2. Condition for uniform velocity ratio of toothed gears

the path of contact and the line of thrust, and the angle ψ which it makes with the common tangent to the pitch circles is called the pressure angle or angle of obliquity.

As the two wheels rotate the point of contact CD may be imagined as a point on an inextensible cord which passes round the base circles and is unwound from B as it is wound on to A. The velocity of the point of contact along the path of contact is thus equal to the peripheral velocity of the base circles.

4.3. Definitions and Tooth Proportions

Pitch circle. When two gear wheels are in correct mesh the pitch circles touch at the pitch point, which lies on the line of centres as shown in Fig. 4.2.

Base circle. This is the circle from which the involute profile of the teeth is generated. It will be seen from Fig. 4.2 that

$$\frac{\text{base circle radius}}{\text{pitch circle radius}} = \cos \psi$$

where ψ = pressure angle or angle of obliquity.

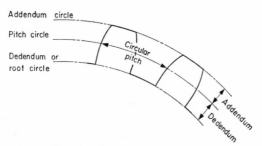

Fig. 4.3. Dimensions of gear teeth

Addendum. The radial height of the tooth above the pitch circle.

Dedendum. The radial depth of the tooth below the pitch circle.

The addendum circle passes through the top of the teeth and the dedendum or root circle passes through the base of the teeth.

Working depth. The sum of the addenda of two mating teeth.

Circular pitch. The distance measured round the pitch circle between corresponding points on adjacent teeth $= \pi d/t$.

Diametral pitch. The number of teeth in a wheel per inch of pitch diameter $= t/d$.

Module. The reciprocal of the diametral pitch $= d/t$, where

$$d = \text{pitch circle diameter,}$$
$$t = \text{number of teeth.}$$

Note that circular pitch $\times$ diametral pitch $= (\pi d/t) \times (t/d) = \pi$.

Standard proportions. The following proportions are recommended by the British Standards Institution in B.S.S. 436—1940:

$$addendum = \frac{1}{\text{diametral pitch}},$$

$$dedendum = \frac{1\cdot25}{\text{diametral pitch}},$$

$$pressure\ angle = 20°.$$

4.4. Interference

For correct tooth action giving uniform velocity ratio it is clear from section 4.2 that contact between two mating teeth must be confined to the involute profiles, i.e. contact must occur only outside the base circles. If, due to the addendum of

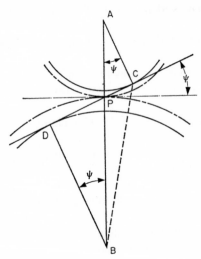

FIG. 4.4. Interference of gear teeth—two wheels

one tooth being too large, contact occurs inside the base circle, undercutting of the other tooth will take place causing "interference".

In Fig. 4.4, A and B are the centres of two wheels in gear, P is the pitch point and C and D are the points at which the common tangent touches the respective base circles. It is clear that if interference is to be avoided the radius of the addendum circle of wheel A must not be greater than AD, and that of wheel B must not be greater than BC. It is also clear from Fig. 4.4 that if the same addendum is to be used for both wheels, the length of BC will be the limiting factor.

Let R_A and R_B = pitch circle radii of the respective wheels,
$\quad\quad\quad a$ = addendum,

then to avoid interference

$$R_B + a \leqslant BC,$$

$$BC = \sqrt{(BD^2 + DC^2)}$$

$$= \sqrt{(R_B \cos \Psi)^2 + (R_A \sin \Psi + R_B \sin \Psi)^2}$$

$$= \sqrt{R_B{}^2 \cos^2 \Psi + R_A{}^2 \sin^2 \Psi + 2R_A R_B \sin^2 \Psi + R_B{}^2 \sin^2 \Psi}$$

$$= \sqrt{R_B{}^2 + 2R_A R_B \sin^2 + R_A{}^2 \sin^2}. \tag{4.1}$$

If t_A = number of teeth in A (the smaller wheel),

$$G = \text{gear ratio} = \frac{R_B}{R_A},$$

then

$$\frac{Gt_A}{2} + a \leqslant \sqrt{\left(\frac{G^2 t_A{}^2}{4} + \frac{2G t_A{}^2}{4} \sin^2 \psi + \frac{t_A{}^2 \sin^2 \psi}{4}\right)},$$

$$G + \frac{2a}{t_A} \leqslant \sqrt{(G^2 + (2G + 1) \sin^2 \psi)},$$

$$\frac{2a}{t_A} \leqslant \sqrt{(G^2 + (2G + 1) \sin^2 \psi)} - G. \tag{4.2}$$

From this result it will be seen that for given values of the gear ratio and the pressure angle there is a maximum value for the ratio a/t_A which will avoid interference.

If a standard addendum is used there is a minimum number of teeth which the smaller wheel can have to avoid interference.

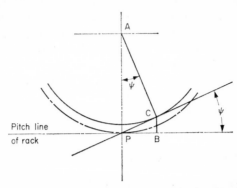

FIG. 4.5. Interference of gear teeth—wheel and rack

Rack and Pinion

In Fig. 4.5, P is the pitch point, i.e. the point of contact of the pitch circle of the pinion A with the pitch line of the rack, and PC is the line of thrust tangential to the base circle of wheel A at C. The rack teeth will have straight sides inclined at an angle $(90° - \psi)$ to the pitch line.

To avoid interference, the addendum of the rack teeth must not be greater than BC, i.e.

$$a \leqslant R_A \sin^2 \psi$$

or

$$R_A \geqslant \frac{a}{\sin^2 \psi}. \tag{4.3}$$

WORKED EXAMPLE

4.1. Two gear wheels mesh externally giving a velocity ratio

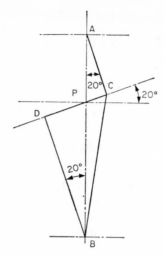

FIG. 4.6. Diagram for worked example 4.1

of 2. The teeth are of involute shape having a diametral pitch of 5 and pressure angle of 20°. The tooth addendum for both wheels is 0·2 in. Determine the minimum number of teeth in the smaller wheel if interference is to be avoided.

SOLUTION

Figure 4.6 shows the essential geometry of the problem.

AP and BP are the respective pitch circle radii.

DC is the line of thrust tangential to the two base circles.

To avoid interference the radius of the addendum circle of wheel B must not exceed BC.

Let

$$AP = R_A,$$
$$BP = R_B = 2R_A,$$
$$BC^2 = BD^2 + DC^2,$$
$$(2R_A + 0·2)^2 = (2R_A \cos 20°)^2 + (3R_A \sin 20°)^2.$$

This results in the quadratic equation

$$R_A^2 - 1.38\, R_A - 0.069 = 0$$

from which

$$R_A = 1.43 \text{ in.}$$

Number of teeth $= 2 \times 1.43 \times 5 = 14.3$, i.e. **15 teeth.**

4.5. Velocity of Sliding

Referring again to Fig. 4.2 the velocity of sliding of the tooth profiles at the point of contact will be equal to $v_{CD} = v_{DC}$. The relative motion of the two wheels has been shown to be that of rotation about P and the relative angular velocity will be the difference of the angular velocities of the wheels, i.e.

$$\omega_{AB} = \omega_A - \omega_B,$$

hence

$$V_{CD} = PC\,(\omega_A - \omega_B). \tag{4.4}$$

It should be noted that ω_A and ω_B have opposite directions and will therefore be of opposite sign. The algebraic difference $(\omega_A - \omega_B)$ will thus, in fact, be the arithmetic sum of the numerical values of the angular velocities.

4.6. Path of Contact and Arc of Contact

In Fig. 4.7 the pressure angle has been exaggerated in order to make the diagram clear. If the wheels are rotating in the directions shown, A being the driver, contact between mating teeth will begin at the point F, where the addendum circle of wheel A cuts the pressure line, and will cease at the point E, where the addendum circle of wheel B cuts the pressure line. It is assumed that the addendum is less than the maximum permissible value to avoid interference.

FP is called the path of approach, PE the path of recess and the total length FE is the path of contact.

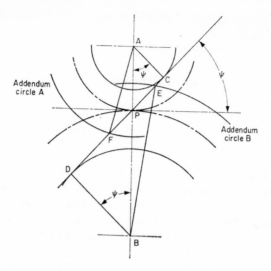

Fig. 4.7. Path of contact

$$FP = \sqrt{(AF^2 - AC^2)} - PC$$

$$= \sqrt{[(R_A + a)^2 - R_A^2 \cos^2 \psi]} - R_A \sin \psi, \quad (4.5)$$

$$PE = \sqrt{(BE^2 - BD^2)} - DP$$

$$= \sqrt{[(R_B + a)^2 - R_B^2 \cos^2 \psi]} - R_B \sin \psi. \quad (4.6)$$

The arc of contact is the amount of rotation of either of the wheels, expressed as a distance measured round the pitch circle, whilst one mating pair of teeth are in contact. From section 4.2 and Fig. 4.2 it will be seen that the peripheral rotation of either of the base circles, whilst this occurs, is equal to the length of the path of contact *FE*. It was shown in section 4.3 that

$$\frac{\text{base circle radius}}{\text{pitch circle radius}} = \cos \psi,$$

hence the arc of contact measured on the pitch circle of either wheel is equal to $FE/\cos\psi$.

By the same reasoning,

$$\text{arc of approach} = \frac{FP}{\cos\psi}$$

and

$$\text{arc of recess} = \frac{PE}{\cos\psi}.$$

It is clear that if there is always to be at least one pair of mating teeth in contact, the arc of contact must be at least equal to the circular pitch. The ratio (arc of contact/circular pitch) is called the "contact ratio". The nearest whole numbers above and below this ratio give the greatest and least number of pairs of teeth in contact at any instant.

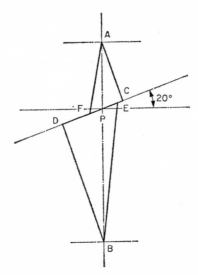

Fig. 4.8. Diagram for worked example 4.2

WORKED EXAMPLE

4.2. Using the information in example 4.1 determine the maximum velocity of sliding of the tooth profiles, and the contact ratio. The larger wheel rotates at 250 rev/min.

SOLUTION

Referring to Fig. 4.8, AF and BE are the radii of the addendum circles of wheels A and B respectively.

$$AF = R_A + a = 1{\cdot}5 + 0{\cdot}2 = 1{\cdot}7 \text{ in.}$$

$$BE = R_B + a = 3{\cdot}0 + 0{\cdot}2 = 3{\cdot}2 \text{ in.}$$

$$PE = DE - DP$$

$$= \sqrt{(BE^2 - BD^2)} - DP$$

$$= \sqrt{(3{\cdot}2^2 - 3{\cdot}0^2 \cos^2 20°)} - 3{\cdot}0 \sin 20°$$

$$= \sqrt{(10{\cdot}24 - 7{\cdot}95)} - 1{\cdot}03$$

$$= 1{\cdot}51 - 1{\cdot}03 = 0{\cdot}48 \text{ in.}$$

$$PF = CF - CP$$

$$= \sqrt{(AF^2 - AC^2)} - CP$$

$$= \sqrt{(1{\cdot}7^2 - 1{\cdot}5^2 \cos^2 20°)} - 1{\cdot}5 \sin 20°$$

$$= \sqrt{(2{\cdot}89 - 1{\cdot}99)} - 0{\cdot}51$$

$$= 0{\cdot}95 - 0{\cdot}51 = 0{\cdot}44 \text{ in.}$$

Maximum velocity of sliding will occur at E and

$$= (\omega_A - \omega_B) PE$$

$$= 3\omega_B \,.\, PE$$

$$= 3 \times \frac{2\pi \times 250}{60} \times 0{\cdot}48$$

$$= \mathbf{38{\cdot}5 \text{ in/sec.}}$$

Length of path of contact $= FP + PE = 0.92$ in.

Length of arc of contact on pitch circle $= \dfrac{0.92}{\cos 20°} = 0.98$ in.

$$\text{Circular pitch} = \frac{\pi}{5} = 0.63 \text{ in.}$$

$$\text{Contact Ratio} = \frac{0.98}{0.63} = \mathbf{1.55}.$$

4.7. Effect of Varying the Centre Distance of Two Gears

Since the path of contact or line of thrust is the common tangent to the base circles of the wheels, it will be seen on referring to Fig. 4.6 that any variation in the distance between the centres of the wheels will alter the pressure angle ψ. Increasing the centre distance will produce an increase in ψ and vice versa. At the same time, with an increase in the centre distance, the points E and F, where the respective addendum circles cut the line of thrust, will move closer to the pitch point P thereby reducing the length of the path of contact. This will have no ill effect on the tooth action provided the arc of contact is not thereby reduced to a value less than the circular pitch. Since the pitch circle diameters are proportional to the base circle diameters there will be no change in the gear ratio.

Similarly, the centre distance may be decreased provided that (a) interference is not caused due to the point E passing beyond C, and (b) the tops of the teeth on one wheel do not foul the roots of the teeth on the other wheel.

4.8. Compound Gear Trains

This section is included merely for the sake of completeness and may be omitted by students who have already dealt with the subject in an earlier course.

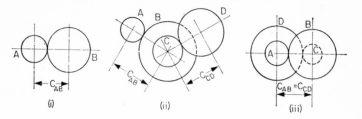

FIG. 4.9. Simple and compound gear trains

Figure 4.9 shows (i) a simple train, (ii) a compound train and (iii) a reverted train.

Let t_A, t_B, t_C, etc., be the numbers of teeth in the respective wheels,

S = diametral pitch of the teeth,

C_{AB} = centre distance of wheels A and B, etc.,

d_A, d_B, d_C, etc., be the pitch circle diameters of the respective wheels.

In the simple gear train,

$$C_{AB} = \tfrac{1}{2}(d_A + d_B) = \tfrac{1}{2}\left(\frac{t_A}{S} + \frac{t_B}{S}\right)$$

$$= \frac{1}{2S}(t_A + t_B). \qquad (4.7)$$

$$\text{Gear ratio} = \frac{t_A}{t_B} = -\frac{\omega_B}{\omega_A} \text{ or } \frac{\omega_B}{\omega_A} = -\frac{t_A}{t_B}. \qquad (4.8)$$

The negative sign indicates that the wheels rotate in opposite directions. Similarly, in the compound train,

$$\left. \begin{aligned} C_{AB} &= \frac{1}{2S}(t_A + t_B) \\[2mm] C_{CD} &= \frac{1}{2S}(t_C + t_D) \end{aligned} \right\}. \qquad (4.9)$$

Therefore,

$$\frac{\omega_B}{\omega_A} \times \frac{\omega_D}{\omega_C} = \frac{\omega_B}{\omega_A} \times \frac{\omega_D}{\omega_B} = -\frac{t_A}{t_B} \times -\frac{t_C}{t_D}.$$

or

$$\frac{\omega_D}{\omega_A} = \frac{t_A}{t_B} \times \frac{t_C}{t_D}. \tag{4.10}$$

In the reverted train the two centre distances are equal, i.e.

$$C_{AB} = C_{CD}.$$

Therefore

$$\frac{1}{2S}(t_A + t_B) = \frac{1}{2S}(t_C + t_D),$$

$$t_A + t_B = t_C + t_D. \tag{4.11}$$

As for the compound train,

$$\frac{\omega_D}{\omega_A} = \frac{t_A}{t_B} \times \frac{t_C}{t_D}. \tag{4.12}$$

WORKED EXAMPLE

4.3. Two parallel shafts are to be connected by two alternative pairs of gears to give two velocity ratios. Shaft L, which rotates at 750 rev/min, carries the wheels A and B. Shaft M carries the wheels C and D and the numbers of teeth are to be such that when A gears with C, the shaft M rotates at 400 rev/min, and when B gears with D, approximately 300 rev/min. The diametral pitch of the teeth of all wheels is to be 4 and the centre distance of the shafts is to be about 14 in.

Determine suitable numbers of teeth for all the wheels, the actual centre distance and the actual speed of M when B and D are in mesh.

SOLUTION

$$t_A + t_B = t_C + t_D = 112 \text{ approx.} \qquad (1)$$

$$\frac{t_A}{t_B} = \frac{400}{750} = \frac{8}{15}. \qquad (2)$$

$$\frac{t_C}{t_D} = \frac{300}{750} = \frac{2}{5}, \qquad (3)$$

From equations (1) and (2)

$$t_A + t_B = n(8 + 15) = 23n = 112 \text{ approx.}$$

The nearest integral value of $n = 5$, giving

$$t_A = \mathbf{40} \text{ and } t_B = \mathbf{75.}$$

Thus

$$t_C + t_D = t_A + t_B = 115.$$

Hence

$$t_C = \frac{2}{7} \times 115 = 32\frac{6}{7}$$

and

$$t_D = \frac{5}{7} \times 115 = 82\frac{1}{7}.$$

But t_C and t_D must be integers, therefore make $t_C = \mathbf{33}$ and $t_D = \mathbf{82.}$

$$\text{Actual centre distance} = \frac{115}{8} = \mathbf{14\frac{3}{8} \text{ in.}}$$

Actual speed of M when C and D are engaged $= 750 \times 33/82$ $= \mathbf{302 \text{ rev/min.}}$

4.9. Epicyclic Gear Trains

An epicyclic gear train is one in which the centre of rotation of at least one of the wheels of the train rotates in a circle about the main axis. For this reason the term "sun and planet" gear is sometimes used.

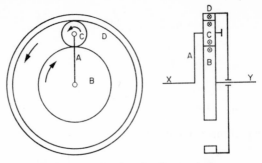

Fig. 4.10. Simple epicyclic gear train

Figure 4.10 shows diagrammatically the arrangement of a simple epicyclic gear train. On the shaft X is mounted an arm A carrying the wheel C which can rotate freely on its spindle. Wheel B is fixed to the shaft Y. Wheel C meshes externally with wheel B and internally with the annular wheel D which is free to rotate on the shaft Y.

Let ω_A = angular velocity of the arm A,

$\quad \omega_B, \omega_C, \omega_D$ = angular velocities of B, C and D respectively,

$\quad t_B, t_C, t_D$ = numbers of teeth in wheels B, C and D respectively.

Angular velocity of wheel B relative to arm $A = \omega_{BA} = \omega_B - \omega_A$.

Angular velocity of wheel D relative to arm $A = \omega_{DA} = \omega_D - \omega_A$.

Relative to the arm A, the wheels B, C and D form a simple gear train with an idler C; therefore the ratio of the angular velocities relative to A may be formed by using the theory of the simple train, i.e.

$$\frac{\omega_{DA}}{\omega_{BA}} = -\frac{t_B}{t_C} \times \frac{t_C}{t_D} = -\frac{t_B}{t_D},$$

the negative sign indicating opposite directions of rotation relative to A.

Now

$$\omega_{DA} = \omega_D - \omega_A,$$

$$\omega_{BA} = \omega_B - \omega_A.$$

Therefore

$$\frac{\omega_D - \omega_A}{\omega_B - \omega_A} = -\frac{t_B}{t_D} \qquad (4.13)$$

The relative directions of rotation may be shown in the sectional view on the right of Fig. 4.10 by using the electrical convention for indicating the direction of current in a wire, viz.,

$\odot$ indicates motion towards the observer,
$\otimes$ indicates motion away from the observer.

This shows clearly that ω_{DA} and ω_{BA} are opposite in direction. This convention may not be necessary in this simple case but it will be found useful in more complex arrangements.

Figure 4.11 shows a compound epicyclic gear train in which the arm A fixed to the shaft X carries a compound wheel CD of which C meshes with wheel B fixed to shaft Y and D meshes with the annular wheel E which may rotate freely on the shaft Y.

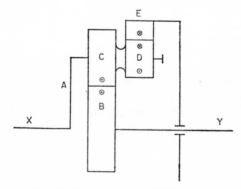

FIG. 4.11. Compound epicyclic gear train

Writing the expression connecting the angular velocities relative to the arm A we have

$$\frac{\omega_E - \omega_A}{\omega_B - \omega_A} = -\frac{t_B}{t_C} \times \frac{t_D}{t_E} \qquad (4.14)$$

the negative sign again indicating opposite directions of relative rotation.

It will be seen that in both the above cases three angular velocities are involved, two of which must be known before the third can be determined. It is usual for one of the wheels (generally the annular wheel) of an epicyclic gear train to be fixed, thus making its angular velocity zero. If this were the case in the above gear trains the equations would reduce to

and

$$\left.\begin{array}{l} \dfrac{O - \omega_A}{\omega_B - \omega_A} = -\dfrac{t_B}{t_D} \\[3mm] \dfrac{O - \omega_A}{\omega_B - \omega_A} = \dfrac{t_B}{t_C} \times \dfrac{t_D}{t_E} \end{array}\right\} \qquad (4.15)$$

or

$$\left.\begin{array}{l} \dfrac{\omega_x}{\omega_y - \omega_x} = \dfrac{t_B}{t_D} \\[3mm] \dfrac{\omega_x}{\omega_y - \omega_x} = \dfrac{t_B}{t_C} \times \dfrac{t_D}{t_E} \end{array}\right\} . \qquad (4.16)$$

WORKED EXAMPLE

4.4. In the gear train shown in Fig. 4.11, the numbers of teeth in the wheels are as follows: B, 40; C, 30; D, 25. If all wheels have teeth of the same pitch, determine the number of teeth in the wheel E and the speed of shaft Y if X rotates at 300 rev/min, and the wheel E is fixed.

SOLUTION

Let R_B, R_C, R_D, R_E be the pitch circle radii,

then

$$R_E = R_B + R_C + R_D.$$

Now the number of teeth in a wheel is proportional to its radius.

Therefore

$$t_E = t_B + t_C + t_D$$
$$= 40 + 30 + 25 = \mathbf{95.}$$

Since speed of rotation in rev/min is proportional to angular velocity in rad/sec, we may write N instead of ω and work in terms of rev/min.

$$\frac{N_E - N_A}{N_B - N_A} = - \frac{t_B}{t_C} \times \frac{t_D}{t_E}.$$

$$N_E = 0,$$

Therefore

$$\frac{0 - N_X}{N_Y - N_X} = - \frac{40}{30} \times \frac{25}{95} = - \frac{20}{57}$$

$$- 57 N_X = - 20 N_X + 20 N_X$$

$$N_Y = \frac{77 N_X}{20} = \frac{77 \times 300}{20} = \mathbf{1155 \ rev/min.}$$

Since the answer is positive the direction of rotation is the same as that of X.

Two-speed Epicyclic Gear Train

Figure 4.12 shows an epicyclic gear train which will provide two different velocity ratios. The arm A fixed to shaft X carries a wheel C which meshes with wheel B fixed to the shaft Y and with the annular wheel D which can rotate freely on shaft Y. Wheel D acts also as an arm carrying a wheel F which meshes with wheel E also fixed to shaft Y and with the annular wheel G which can rotate freely on shaft Y.

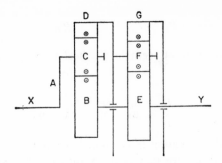

Fig. 4.12. Two-speed epicyclic gear train

Consider first the gear train BCD relative to the arm A and we have

$$\frac{\omega_D - \omega_A}{\omega_B - \omega_A} = -\frac{t_B}{t_D}. \tag{4.17}$$

Now consider the gear train EFG relative to the wheel D and we have

$$\frac{\omega_G - \omega_D}{\omega_E - \omega_D} = -\frac{t_E}{t_G}. \tag{4.18}$$

If, now, the wheel D is fixed making $\omega_D = 0$, equation (4.17) becomes

$$\frac{0 - \omega_A}{\omega_B - \omega_A} = -\frac{t_B}{t_D},$$

or

$$\frac{\omega_x}{\omega_y - \omega_x} = \frac{t_B}{t_D}. \tag{4.19}$$

This result is, of course, the same as that obtained for the simple gear first described, and the second train wheels do not affect the velocity ratio.

Now fix the wheel G, thus making $\omega_G = 0$. From equation (4.18) we get

$$\frac{0 - \omega_D}{\omega_E - \omega_D} = -\frac{t_E}{t_G}.$$

From this equation we obtain a value for ω_D in terms of ω_E, t_E and t_G, viz.

$$\omega_D = \frac{\omega_E t_E}{t_G + t_E}. \tag{4.20}$$

This value of ω_D can now be substituted in equation (4.17) from which the new value of the velocity ratio may be found.

WORKED EXAMPLE

4.5. In the arrangement shown in Fig. 4.12, $t_B = t_E = 50$, $t_C = t_F = 30$. Find the number of teeth in wheels D and G.

If the shaft Y rotates at 1000 rev/min, find the speed of shaft X, (a) if wheel D is fixed, (b) if wheel G is fixed.

SOLUTION

$$R_G = R_D = R_B + 2R_C$$

$$t_G = t_D + 2t_C = 50 + 60 = \mathbf{110}.$$

$$\frac{N_D - N_A}{N_B - N_A} = -\frac{t_B}{t_D} = -\frac{50}{110} = -\frac{5}{11}. \tag{1}$$

$$\frac{N_G - N_D}{N_E - N_D} = -\frac{t_E}{t_G} = -\frac{5}{11}. \tag{2}$$

(a) If D is fixed, $N_D = 0$.

Substituting in equation (1) above,

$$\frac{0 - N_X}{N_Y - N_X} = -\frac{5}{11}.$$

$$-11 N_X = -5N_Y + 5 N_X$$

$$N_X = \frac{5}{16} N_Y = \mathbf{312{\cdot}5 \ rev/min}$$

in the same direction as N_Y.

(b) If G is fixed, $N_G = 0$.

Substituting in equation (2) above,

$$\frac{0 - N_D}{N_Y - N_D} = -\frac{5}{11}$$

from which

$$N_D = \frac{5}{16} N_Y = 312 \cdot 5.$$

Now substitute for N_D in equation (1) above,

$$\frac{312 \cdot 5 - N_X}{N_Y - N_X} = -\frac{5}{11}$$

$$3443 - 11 N_X = -5 N_Y + 5 N_X = -5000 + 5 N_X$$

$$N_X = \frac{8443}{16} = \mathbf{527 \ rev/min}$$

in the same direction as N_Y.

Epicyclic Gear Train using Bevel Gears

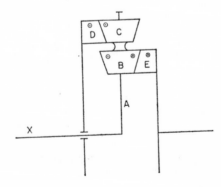

Fig. 4.13. Epicyclic bevel gear train

Figure 4.13 shows an epicyclic gear train which makes use of bevel gears. The arm A, fixed to the shaft X, carries the compound wheel BC of which C meshes with wheel D and B with wheel E fixed to the shaft Y.

Consider the gear train relative to the arm A, then

$$\frac{\omega_E - \omega_A}{\omega_D - \omega_A} = -\frac{t_D}{t_C} \times \frac{t_B}{t_E}$$

If, now, the wheel D is fixed, making $\omega_D = 0$, we get

$$\frac{\omega_E - \omega_A}{0 - \omega_A} = -\frac{t_D}{t_C} \times \frac{t_B}{t_E}$$

or

$$\frac{\omega_y - \omega_x}{\omega_x} = \frac{t_D}{t_C} \times \frac{t_B}{t_E}. \tag{4.21}$$

WORKED EXAMPLE

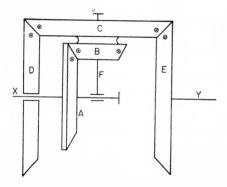

FIG. 4.14. Epicyclic bevel gear train

4.6. In the gear train shown in Fig. 4.14, the wheel A, fixed to the shaft X, gears with wheel B. Wheels B and C form a compound wheel which can rotate freely on the pin F, which in turn can rotate freely about X. Wheel C gears with D which is fixed and with E which is keyed to the shaft Y. If X rotates at 200 rev/min, determine the speed of rotation of Y.

The numbers of teeth in the wheels are: A, 20; B, 25; C, 50; D, 60; E, 60.

SOLUTION

$$\frac{N_A - N_F}{N_E - N_F} = -\frac{t_E}{t_C} \times \frac{t_B}{t_A} = -\frac{6}{5} \times \frac{25}{20} = -\frac{3}{2}, \qquad (1)$$

$$\frac{N_D - N_F}{N_E - N_F} = -\frac{t_E}{t_D} = -\frac{60}{60} = -1. \qquad (2)$$

Since D is fixed, put $N_D = 0$ in equation (2).

$$\frac{0 - N_F}{N_E - N_F} = -1$$

$$-N_F = 2 N_E.$$

Now substitute for N_F in equation (1)

$$\frac{N_A - 2N_E}{N_E - 2N_E} = -\frac{3}{2}$$

or

$$\frac{N_X - 2N_Y}{-N_Y} = -\frac{3}{2}$$

$$2N_X - 4N_Y = 3N_Y.$$
$$7N_Y = 2N_X$$

$$N_Y = \frac{2}{7} N_X = \frac{2}{7} \times 200 = \textbf{57·1 rev/min}$$

in the same direction as N_X.

Examples

4.7. A pinion of 20 involute teeth and 5 in. pitch circle diameter drives a rack. The addendum of both pinion and rack is $\frac{1}{4}$ in. What is the least pressure angle which can be used to avoid undercutting? With this pressure angle find the length of the arc of contact and the minimum number of teeth in contact at a time.

Answer: 18·1°, 1·39 in., 1 pair.

(L.U. 1949)

4.8. A pinion 12 in. p.c.d. meshes with a gear wheel 48 in. p.c.d. The teeth are of involute form, 2 d.p. and 25° angle of obliquity. Addendum for each wheel is 0·5 in. Find the angle that the pinion turns through while any one pair of teeth continue to maintain contact.

If the pinion is the driver and rotates at 200 rev/min, find the velocity of sliding at the instant contact ceases. Prove any formula you use in this latter problem.

Answer: 22·6°, 26·7 in/sec.

(L.U. 1950)

4.9. Two spur wheels having 20 and 40 teeth of involute form mesh externally. The diametral pitch is 4 and the addendum on both wheels is 0·25 in., the pressure angle being 20°.

Determine the maximum velocity of sliding of one tooth over another if the larger wheel runs at 200 rev/min.

Answer: 39·6 in/sec.

(L.U. 1948)

4.10. Two parallel shafts X and Y are to be connected by toothed wheels; wheels A and B form a compound pair which can slide along but rotate with shaft X; wheels C and D are rigidly attached to shaft Y, and the compound pair may be moved so that A engages with C, or B with D.

Shaft X rotates at 640 rev/min, and the speeds of shaft Y are to be 340 rev/min exactly, and 240 rev/min as nearly as possible. Using a diametral pitch of 2 for all wheels, find the minimum distance between the shaft axes, suitable tooth numbers for the wheels, and the lower speed of Y.

Answer: 51, 96, 40, 107; 239 rev/min.

(L.U. 1949)

4.11. Two shafts A and B in the same line are geared together through an intermediate parallel shaft C. The wheels connecting A and C have a diametral pitch of 9 and those connecting C and B a pitch of 4, the least number of teeth in any wheel being not less than 15. The speed of B is to be about but not greater than 1/12 the speed of A and the ratio at each reduction is the same. Find suitable wheels, the actual reduction and the distance of shaft C from A and B.

Answer: 58, 74, 26, 90; 1/12·1; 14·5.   ·(I.Mech.E. 1950)

4.12. In the gear drive indicated in Fig. 4.15, A is the driving shaft rotating at 300 rev/min in the direction shown, and B is the driving shaft. The casing C is held stationary. E and H are keyed to the central vertical spindle, F can rotate freely on this spindle. K and L are rigidly fixed to each other and

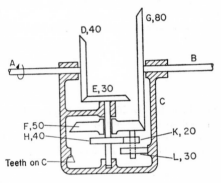

Fig. 4.15. Epicyclic bevel gear train for example 4.12

rotate together freely on a pin fitted on the underside of F. L meshes with internal teeth on the casing C.

The diametral pitch of the teeth on H and L is 4, and the numbers of teeth on the various wheels are as shown.

Find the number of teeth on C, and the speed and direction of rotation of B.

Answer: 90, 100 rev/min opposite to A.   (L.U. 1950)

4.13. In the epicyclic gear train shown in Fig. 4.16, the numbers of teeth in the wheels are: A, 50; B, 20; C, 90; D, 30; E, 30; F, 90; and either of the wheels C and F may be fixed.

Determine for both these cases the velocity ratio N_Y/N_X.

Answer: +2·8, +1·93.

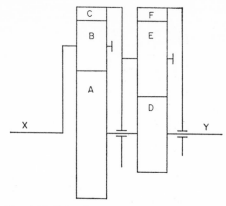

Fig. 4.16. Epicyclic gear train for example 4.13

4.14. Figure 4.17 shows an epicyclic bevel train in which the driving shaft *G* rotates at 200 rev/min. The numbers of teeth in the wheels are: *A*, 40; *B*, 19; *C*, 29; *D*, 57. Determine the speed of the shaft *E* if the wheel *D* is fixed.

Answer: 103 rev/min in same direction as *G*.

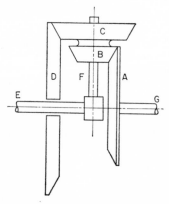

Fig. 4.17. Epicyclic bevel gear train for example 4.14

D

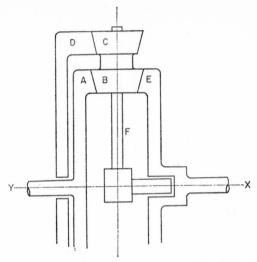

Fig. 4.18. Epicyclic bevel gear train for example 4.15

4.15. In the epicyclic gear train shown in Fig. 4.18 the shaft X rotates at 1400 rev/min and the wheel D is fixed. The numbers of teeth in the wheels are: A, 75; B, 25; C, 30; D, 120; E, 75. Determine the speed of the shaft Y.

Answer: 200 rev/min in opposite direction to X.

CHAPTER FIVE

DRY FRICTION

5.1. Introduction

Readers of this book will already be familiar with the so-called laws of dry or solid friction, but for the sake of completeness they will be stated here.

The force of friction exerted between two dry surfaces in contact, which slide or tend to slide relatively is:

   (i) independent of the area of contact,
   (ii) independent of the velocity of sliding,
   (iii) dependent on the nature and material of the surfaces,
   (iv) proportional to the normal reaction between the surfaces.

Thus for a given pair of surfaces in contact, if

N = normal reaction,
F = friction force,

then

$$F \propto N$$

or

$$F = \mu N,$$

where μ is a constant for a given pair of surfaces, and is called the coefficient of friction.

It should be noted that the above "laws" have no rational foundation and are based purely on experimental evidence. Nevertheless, their application to actual problems gives results which are sufficiently true for most practical purposes.

Another point which is often overlooked by students is that the friction force acts only when some other force is applied which overcomes or tends to overcome the friction force. Thus, if a block is resting on a horizontal surface no friction force acts until a horizontal force or component is applied to the block. If this applied force is gradually increased from zero, the frictional resisting force will also increase and will be equal to the applied force until the latter reaches the value of the limiting frictional force, i.e. μN. Any further increase in the applied force will produce accelerated motion.

The analyses which follow assume that the limiting condition operates, i.e. that relative sliding between the surfaces in contact is taking place or is on the point of doing so.

5.2. Resultant Reaction

It is convenient in many friction problems to combine the normal reaction with the friction force giving a resultant reaction R as shown in Fig. 5.1.

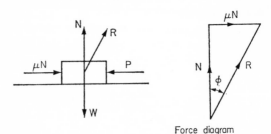

Fig. 5.1. Resultant reaction at sliding surfaces

This reaction R will be inclined to the normal at an angle ϕ, called the angle of friction, in such a way as to oppose the relative sliding. From the force diagram it will be seen that $\tan \phi = \mu N/N = \mu$.

5.3. Inclined Plane

(a) Body moving up the plane

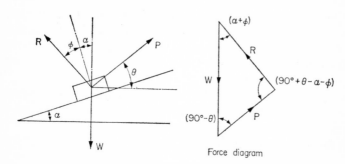

Fig. 5.2. Inclined plane friction—body moving up the plane

A block of weight W resting on a plane inclined at an angle α to the horizontal is acted on by a force P inclined at an angle θ to the horizontal which tends to move the body up the plane. The resultant reaction R will be inclined as shown, at an angle ϕ to the normal to the plane. The three forces W, P and R will be in equilibrium as shown by the force diagram.

Applying the sine rule, we have

$$\frac{P}{\sin (\alpha + \phi)} = \frac{W}{\sin (90° + \theta - \alpha - \phi)},$$

or

$$\frac{P}{\sin (\alpha + \phi)} = \frac{W}{\cos (\theta - \alpha - \phi)},$$

therefore

$$P = \frac{W \sin (\alpha + \phi)}{\cos (\theta - \alpha - \phi)}. \tag{5.1}$$

Two special cases may occur in practice, viz., (i) when P is parallel to the plane making $\theta = \alpha$ and (ii) when P is horizontal making $\theta = 0$.

(i) Putting $\theta = \alpha$, we have

$$P = \frac{W \sin (\alpha + \phi)}{\cos (-\phi)} = \frac{W \sin (\alpha + \phi)}{\cos \phi}. \qquad (5.2)$$

(ii) Putting $\theta = 0$, we have

$$P = \frac{W \sin (\alpha + \phi)}{\cos (-\alpha - \phi)} = \frac{W \sin (\alpha + \phi)}{\cos (\alpha + \phi)} = W \tan (\alpha + \phi). \qquad (5.3)$$

(*b*) *Body moving down the plane*

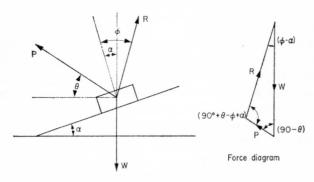

Force diagram

FIG. 5.3. Inclined plane friction—body moving down the plane

If the force P is applied so as to tend to move the body down the plane, the reaction R will be inclined on the opposite side of the normal as shown in Fig. 5.3. Applying the sine rule to the force diagram, we have

$$\frac{P}{\sin (\phi - \alpha)} = \frac{W}{\sin (90° + \theta - \phi + \alpha)}$$

or

$$\frac{P}{\sin (\phi - \alpha)} = \frac{W}{\cos (\theta - \phi + \alpha)} \,.$$

Therefore

$$P = \frac{W \sin (\phi - \alpha)}{\cos (\theta - \phi + \alpha)} \,. \tag{5.4}$$

In the figure the friction angle ϕ is shown to be greater than the inclination of the plane α.

If α is equal to ϕ, then substituting this value in equation (5.4) we obtain

$$P = \frac{W \sin (\phi - \phi)}{\cos (\theta - \phi + \phi)} = 0,$$

i.e. the body is in equilibrium under the action of W and R and if it is given a slight push down the plane it will continue to descend with uniform velocity.

If α is greater than ϕ, then

$$P = \frac{W \sin (\phi - \alpha)}{\cos (\theta - \phi + \alpha)}$$

will be negative, i.e. a force P in a direction opposite to that shown in the figure will have to be applied to prevent the body from sliding down the plane.

Consider again the two special cases in which (i) P is parallel to the plane, i.e. $\theta = -\alpha$, and (ii) P is horizontal, i.e. $\theta = 0$.

(i) Putting $\theta = -\alpha$, we have

$$P = \frac{W \sin (\phi - \alpha)}{\cos (-\alpha - \phi + \alpha)} = \frac{W \sin (\phi - \alpha)}{\cos \phi} \,. \tag{5.5}$$

(ii) Putting $\theta = 0$, we have

$$P = \frac{W \sin (\phi - \alpha)}{\cos (-\phi + \alpha)} = \frac{W \sin (\phi - \alpha)}{\cos (\phi - \alpha)} = W \tan (\phi - \alpha). \tag{5.6}$$

5.4. Wedge Friction

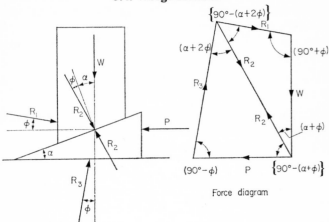

Fig. 5.4. Wedge friction—body being raised

Figure 5.4 shows a block of weight W which is raised vertically by means of a wedge of angle α resting on a horizontal surface, the block being guided by a vertical surface. Let the coefficient of friction, $\mu = \tan \phi$, be the same for all pairs of surfaces.

Consider first the forces acting on the block. They will be:

W, the weight of the block acting vertically downwards,

R_1, the resultant reaction at the vertical surface acting in a direction inclined at an angle ϕ to the horizontal and opposing the upward motion of the block,

R_2, the resultant reaction at the upper surface of the wedge, acting in a direction inclined at an angle ϕ to the normal to that surface and opposing the relative motion.

These three forces must be in equilibrium and their vectors will therefore form a closed triangle as shown.

Now consider the forces acting on the wedge. They will be:

R_2, the resultant reaction at the upper surface, equal and opposite to R_2 above,

R_3, the resultant reaction at the lower surface, acting in a direction inclined at an angle ϕ to the vertical and opposing the relative motion,

P, the external force applied in order to raise the block, assumed to be horizontal.

These three forces are in equilibrium and their vectors will also form a closed triangle.

The force diagram shown in Fig. 5.4 combines these two triangles since they have a common side R_2.

Applying the sine rule we have

$$\frac{R_2}{\sin(90 + \phi)} = \frac{W}{\sin 90 - (\alpha + 2\phi)},$$

$$R_2 = \frac{W \cos \phi}{\cos(\alpha + 2\phi)}. \tag{5.7}$$

Also

$$\frac{P}{\sin(\alpha + 2\phi)} = \frac{R_2}{\sin(90 - \phi)},$$

$$P = \frac{R_2 \sin(\alpha + 2\phi)}{\cos \phi}. \tag{5.8}$$

Combining eqns. (5.7) and (5.8) we have

$$P = \frac{W \cos \phi}{\cos(\alpha + 2\phi)} \times \frac{\sin(\alpha + 2\phi)}{\cos \phi}$$

$$= W \tan(\alpha + 2\phi). \tag{5.9}$$

The same method of analysis may be used to determine the force necessary to withdraw the wedge in order to lower the block.

WORKED EXAMPLE

5.1. A machine part weighing 2 tons slides between vertical guides and is raised and lowered by means of a wedge placed under the part. The angle of the wedge is 5° and the coefficient of friction between all sliding faces is 0·10. Determine the horizontal force which must be applied to the wedge in order to (a) raise, (b) lower the machine part.

SOLUTION

(a) $a = 5°$, $\tan \phi = 0·10$, $\phi = 5°43'$.

From equation (5.9)

$$P = W \tan (a + 2\phi)$$

$$= 2 \times 2240 \times \tan 16°26'$$

$$= 2 \times 2240 \times 0·295$$

$$= \textbf{1320 lb.}$$

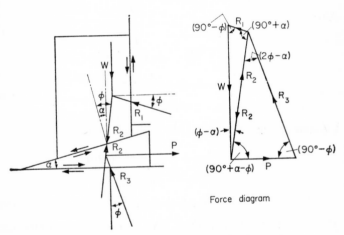

FIG. 5.5. Wedge friction—body being lowered

(b) Referring to Fig. 5.5, since the wedge is being withdrawn to the right the machine part will bear against the right-hand vertical guide and the reactions at the faces will be as shown.

From the force diagram,

$$\frac{P}{\sin(2\phi - \alpha)} = \frac{R_2}{\sin(90 - \phi)} = \frac{W}{\sin(90 + \alpha)},$$

hence

$$P = \frac{W \sin(2\phi - \alpha)}{\cos \alpha}$$

$$= \frac{2 \times 2240 \times \sin 6°26'}{\cos 5°}$$

$$= \frac{2 \times 2240 \times 0\cdot112}{0\cdot996}$$

$$= \textbf{503 lb.}$$

5.5. Screw Thread Friction

(a) *Square thread*

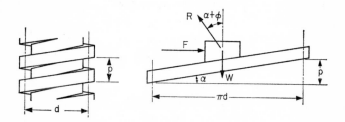

FIG. 5.6. Friction of a square thread

Let d = mean diameter of the thread,

  p = pitch of the thread, i.e. the axial distance moved by the nut for 1 revolution of the screw—this is sometimes known as the lead.

It will be clear from Fig. 5.6 that the motion of the nut relative to thread is similar to that of a body sliding on an inclined plane of angle a, where $\tan a = p/\pi d$. Tightening of the nut will be equivalent to pushing the body up the plane, and slackening will be equivalent to pushing it down the plane.

Let W = axial load on the nut,

         P = tangential force applied at the mean radius of the thread perpendicular to the axis.

It will be seen that W and P are respectively equivalent to the weight of the body on the plane and the horizontal force applied to it. The relation between P and W for tightening is given by equation (5.3), viz.,

$$P = W \tan (a + \phi). \tag{5.10}$$

This relation may be expressed in terms of p, d and μ by expanding the tangent term, i.e.

$$P = \frac{W (\tan a + \tan \phi)}{1 - \tan a \tan \phi}.$$

Putting $\tan a = \dfrac{p}{\pi d}$ and $\tan \phi = \mu$, we have

$$P = \frac{W [(p/\pi d) + \mu]}{1 - (p/\pi d) \cdot \mu}$$

or

$$P = \frac{W (p + \mu \pi d)}{\pi d - \mu p}. \tag{5.11}$$

If the nut is being slackened then equation (5.6) will apply, i.e.

$$P = W \tan (\phi - a).$$

This relation also may be expressed in terms of p, d, μ, giving

$$P = \frac{W (\mu \pi d - p)}{\mu p - \pi d}. \tag{5.12}$$

It should be noted that if p is greater than $\mu\pi d$ the value of P obtained from equation (5.12) will be negative, i.e. a force must be applied to maintain the nut tightened.

Treating the screw and nut as a simple machine in which W is the load and P the effort, the efficiency will be given by

$$n = \frac{Wp}{P\pi d} = \frac{W \tan \alpha}{P}.$$

Putting

$$P = W \tan (\alpha + \phi),$$

$$\eta = \frac{\tan \alpha}{\tan (\alpha + \phi)}. \tag{5.13}$$

For a given value of the coefficient of friction, $\tan \phi$, the efficiency will vary with the value of α and will have a maximum value when $d\eta/d\alpha = 0$, i.e. when

$$\frac{d}{d\alpha} \cdot \frac{\tan \alpha}{\tan (\alpha + \phi)} = 0.$$

Therefore

$$\sec^2\alpha \tan (\alpha + \phi) - \tan \alpha \sec^2 (\alpha + \phi) = 0,$$

$$\frac{\tan \alpha}{\sec^2\alpha} = \frac{\tan (\alpha + \phi)}{\sec^2 (\alpha + \phi)},$$

$$\sin \alpha \cos \alpha = \sin (\alpha + \phi) \cos (\alpha + \phi),$$

$$\tfrac{1}{2} \sin 2\alpha = \tfrac{1}{2} \sin 2(\alpha + \phi),$$

i.e. $2\alpha = 2 (\alpha + \phi)$ or $180° - 2 (\alpha + \phi)$.

The first root of the equation would give $\phi = 0$; therefore using the second root we have

$$a = 90° - (a + \phi)$$

$$\text{or } 2a = 90° - \phi$$

$$a = 45° - \tfrac{1}{2}\phi.$$

Substituting this value in the expression for efficiency we obtain

$$\eta_{max} = \frac{1 - \sin \phi}{1 + \sin \phi}. \tag{5.14}$$

It should be noted that if the value of a is such that the nut will just remain tight when P is removed, i.e. $a = \phi$, the efficiency of the screw is

$$\eta = \frac{\tan \phi}{\tan 2\phi} \simeq 0{\cdot}5 \text{ if } \phi \text{ is small.}$$

(b) Vee thread

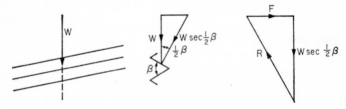

FIG. 5.7. Friction of a vee thread

It will be seen from Fig. 5.7 that the plane normal to the surface of the thread will be inclined at an angle $\tfrac{1}{2}\beta$ to the vertical, where β is the angle of the thread section. The resultant reaction R will act in this plane and the component of W in this plane will be $W \sec \tfrac{1}{2}\beta$.

The force diagram will, therefore, be as shown and

$$F = W \sec \tfrac{1}{2}\beta \tan (a + \phi). \tag{5.15}$$

WORKED EXAMPLE

5.2 A machine bed is inclined at 5° to the horizontal and carries a saddle weighing 120 lb. The saddle is moved along the bed by means of a square threaded screw of $1\frac{1}{2}$ in. mean diameter and $\frac{3}{8}$ in. pitch. The coefficient of friction for all sliding surfaces is 0·075. Determine the torque which must be applied to the screw (a) to move the saddle up the bed, (b) to move it down the bed.

SOLUTION

(a) The force to be exerted by the screw on the saddle is given by equation (5.3)

$$P = \frac{W \sin(\alpha + \phi)}{\cos \phi}$$

$\tan \phi = 0·075$, therefore $\phi = 4·3°$

$$P = \frac{W \sin 9·3°}{\cos 4·3°}$$

$$= \frac{120 \times 0·162}{0·997}$$

$$= 19·5 \text{ lb.}$$

For the screw thread

$$\tan \alpha = \frac{p}{\pi d} = \frac{0·375}{\pi \times 1·5}$$

$$= 0·080,$$

therefore

$$\alpha = 4·6°.$$

Tangential force on screw is given by equation (5.10)

and

$$= 19{\cdot}5 \tan (4{\cdot}6 + 4{\cdot}3)^\circ$$

$$= 19{\cdot}5 \tan 8{\cdot}9^\circ = 19{\cdot}5 \times 0{\cdot}157$$

$$= 3{\cdot}06 \text{ lb.}$$

Torque $= 3{\cdot}06 \times 0{\cdot}75 = \textbf{2·30 lb in.}$

(b) Since $a > \phi$, the saddle must be restrained from accelerating down the plane, and the force will be given by

$$P = \frac{W \sin (a - \phi)}{\cos \phi}$$

$$= \frac{120 \sin 0{\cdot}7^\circ}{\cos 4{\cdot}3^\circ} \quad \frac{120 \times 0{\cdot}012}{0{\cdot}997}$$

$$= 1{\cdot}44 \text{ lb.}$$

Since for the screw thread also, $a > \phi$, a restraining torque must be applied to the screw, and the tangential force is given by

$$1{\cdot}44 \tan (a - \phi) = 1{\cdot}44 \tan 0{\cdot}3^\circ$$

$$= 1{\cdot}44 \times 0{\cdot}005$$

$$= 0{\cdot}0072 \text{ lb.}$$

Torque $= 0{\cdot}0072 \times 0{\cdot}75 = \textbf{0·0054 lb in.}$

5.6. Thrust Bearings

Figure 5.8 shows a truncated conical pivot carrying an axial load W.

Consider an element of the conical surface having a radius r and radial width dr, and let p be the intensity of pressure on the element.

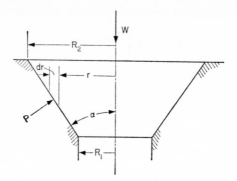

Fig. 5.8. Conical pivot bearing

$$\text{Area of element} = 2\pi r \, \frac{\mathrm{d}r}{\sin \alpha}.$$

$$\text{Normal force on element} = 2\pi p r \, \frac{\mathrm{d}r}{\sin \alpha}.$$

$$\text{Vertical component of normal force} = 2\pi p r \, \frac{\mathrm{d}r}{\sin \alpha} \cdot \sin \alpha$$

$$= 2\pi p r \mathrm{d}r.$$

$$\text{Total vertical force on pivot} = W \int_{R_1}^{R_2} 2\pi p r \mathrm{d}r. \quad (5.16)$$

In order to evaluate this integral we must know how p varies in relation to r.

In the case of a new bearing in which the surfaces have been accurately formed we may assume that the intensity of pressure is uniform, but after the bearing has been in service for some time, wear will have taken place and if the surfaces remain in contact everywhere the rate of wear will be uniform.

Assuming uniform intensity of pressure, we have

$$W = 2\pi p \int_{R_1}^{R_2} r\,\mathrm{d}r$$

$$= p\pi \left(R_2^2 - R_1^2\right)$$

$$= p \times \text{projected area}$$

or

$$p = \frac{W}{\text{projected area}} \cdot \tag{5.17}$$

Assuming uniform rate of wear, then since rate of wear $\propto$ pressure $\times$ velocity $\propto$ pressure $\times$ radius, we have

$$pr = \text{constant, say } C, \text{ or } p = C/r.$$

then

$$W = \int_{R_1}^{R_2} 2\pi(C/r) \cdot r\,\mathrm{d}r$$

$$= 2\pi C \int_{R_1}^{R_2} \mathrm{d}r.$$

$$W = 2\pi C \left(R_2 - R_1\right)$$

or

$$C = \frac{W}{2\pi \left(R_2 - R_1\right)} \cdot \tag{5.18}$$

The friction force on the element of the surface

$$= \text{coefficient of friction} \times \text{normal force}$$

$$= \mu \times 2\pi pr\, \frac{\mathrm{d}r}{\sin \alpha} \cdot$$

Friction torque on element $= \mu \times 2\pi pr\, \dfrac{\mathrm{d}r}{\sin \alpha} \times r$

$$= 2\pi\mu\, pr^2\, \frac{\mathrm{d}r}{\sin \alpha}.$$

Total friction torque on bearing $T = 2\pi\mu \int_{R_1}^{R_2} pr^2 \dfrac{\mathrm{d}r}{\sin \alpha}$.

Assuming uniform pressure,

$$T = \frac{2\pi\mu p}{\sin \alpha} \int_{R_1}^{R_2} r^2 \mathrm{d}r = \frac{2\pi\mu p}{\sin \alpha} \left(\frac{R_2{}^3 - R_1{}^3}{3} \right)$$

and substituting for p from eqn (5.15) we obtain

$$T = \frac{2}{3} \frac{\mu W}{\sin \alpha} \left(\frac{R_2{}^3 - R_1{}^3}{R_2{}^2 - R_1{}^2} \right). \tag{5.19}$$

Assuming uniform wear,

$$T = \frac{2\pi\mu C}{\sin \alpha} \int_{R_1}^{R_2} r \mathrm{d}r = \frac{2\pi\mu C}{\sin \alpha} \left(\frac{R_2{}^2 - R_1{}^2}{2} \right),$$

and substituting for C from eqn (5.16) we obtain

$$T = \frac{\mu W}{2 \sin \alpha} \left(\frac{R_2{}^2 - R_1{}^2}{R_2 - R_1} \right) = \frac{\mu W}{\sin \alpha} \left(\frac{R_2 + R_1}{2} \right).$$

This may be written

$$T = \frac{\mu W}{\sin \alpha} R_m \tag{5.20}$$

where $R_m = $ mean radius of bearing surface.

If $\alpha = 90°$ the bearing becomes a flat collar and since sin $90° = 1$, the term sin α disappears from the two expressions for friction torque in equations (5.19) and (5.20).

It can be shown that whatever the values of R_1 and R_2 the uniform pressure theory gives the greater value of the friction torque, and if there is any doubt as to which should be used it is advisable to apply the uniform pressure theory since any error will be on the safe side.

WORKED EXAMPLE

5.3. A collar thrust bearing has internal and external diameters of 1 in. and 2 in. respectively. The shaft rotates at 300 rev/min and carries an axial load of 150 lb. Compare the friction torque (a) when the bearing and shaft are new with (b) the value when wear has taken place. In the latter case determine the maximum intensity of pressure on the bearing. The coefficient of friction is 0·08.

SOLUTION

(a) Assume that, for the new surfaces, uniform pressure applies.

$$\text{Then friction torque} = \frac{2}{3} \frac{\mu W (R_2^3 - R_1^3)}{(R_2^2 - R_1^2)}$$

$$= \frac{2}{3} \times \frac{0·08 \times 150 (1 - 0·125)}{(1 - 0·25)}$$

$$= \frac{2 \times 0·08 \times 150 \times 0·875}{3 \times 0·75}$$

$$= \textbf{9·33 lb in.}$$

(b) Assuming uniform wear,

$$\text{friction torque} = \mu W R_m$$

$$= 0·08 \times 150 \times 0·75$$

$$= \textbf{9·00 lb in.}$$

From eqn (5.18)

$$p \cdot r = C = \frac{W}{2\pi (R_2 - R_1)}$$

$$= \frac{150}{2\pi (1 - 0·5)} = \textbf{47·8.}$$

Maximum pressure occurs at the minimum radius, therefore

$$\text{maximum pressure} = \frac{47 \cdot 8}{0 \cdot 5} = \textbf{95·6 lb/in}^2.$$

5.7. Journal Bearings

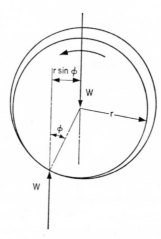

FIG. 5.9. Journal bearing

Figure 5.9 shows a shaft of radius r rotating counterclockwise in a journal bearing, the clearance between the shaft and bearing being very much exaggerated. The shaft carries a vertical load W acting through the axis of rotation.

As the shaft rotates, friction at the line of contact with the bearing will cause it to roll up to the left until a point is reached at which relative sliding takes place. At this point the reaction between the surfaces, which must be equal and opposite to it, will be inclined at an angle ϕ to the normal to the surfaces at the point of contact, where $\tan \phi = \mu$.

The friction torque on the shaft will be equal to the couple formed by the vertically downward load W and the vertically upward reaction. This couple is given by

$$T = Wr \sin \phi. \tag{5.21}$$

For small values of ϕ, $\sin \phi = \tan \phi$ and the equation may be written

$$T = \mu Wr. \tag{5.22}$$

5.8. Friction Clutches

The analysis of the action of a friction clutch, conical or flat plate, is precisely the same as that used in the case of the thrust bearing. The maximum torque will be transmitted by the clutch when the surfaces in contact are on the point of slipping and limiting friction is operating. The conical clutch will have only one pair of operating surfaces but the flat plate clutch may have more than one pair. If there are n effective pairs of surfaces in contact, the torque transmitted will be n times that for a single pair since the axial thrust is applied to all the surfaces.

The choice of which theory to use, constant pressure or constant wear, again depends on the state of the surfaces but, in the absence of any information, that theory which gives the lower friction torque, i.e. the uniform wear theory, should be used since any error will then be on the safe side.

WORKED EXAMPLE

5.4. A cone clutch has an included angle of 60° and is required to transmit 10 h.p. at 500 rev/min. The coefficient of friction is 0·35 and the intensity of normal pressure is not to exceed 30 lb/in². If the ratio of the extreme diameters is to be 3/2 determine these diameters and the axial load which is required.

SOLUTION

$$\text{Torque} = \frac{10 \times 33,000 \times 12}{2\pi \times 500} = 1260 \text{ lb in.}$$

also

$$\text{torque} = \frac{\mu W R_m}{\sin \alpha}, \quad \text{where } \alpha = 30^\circ,$$

$$W R_m = \frac{1260 \times 0\cdot5}{0\cdot35} = 1800 \text{ lb in.} \qquad (1)$$

Let R_1 and R_2 be the smaller and larger radii. Then, from equation (5.18),

$$C = p \cdot r = \frac{W}{2\pi (R_2 - R_1)},$$

and since maximum pressure occurs at the minimum radius,

$$30 R_1 = \frac{W}{2\pi (R_2 - R_1)}.$$

From equation (1) above,

$$W = \frac{1800 \times 2}{R_1 + R_2}$$

and putting $R_1 = \frac{2}{3} R_2$ we obtain

$$\frac{30 \times 2R_2}{3} = \frac{1800 \times 2}{2\pi (R_2{}^2 - R_1{}^2)} = \frac{1800 \times 2}{2\pi [1 - (4/9)] R_2{}^2},$$

$$R_2{}^3 = \frac{1800 \times 2 \times 3 \times 9}{60 \times 2\pi \times 5} = 51\cdot6,$$

$$R_2 = 3\cdot73 \text{ in.,}$$

$$R_1 = 2\cdot49 \text{ in.,}$$

i.e. the required diameters are say 7·5 in. and 5 in.

$$W = \frac{1800 \times 2}{R_1 + R_2} = \frac{1800 \times 2}{6 \cdot 21}$$

$$= \mathbf{580 \ lb.}$$

5.9. Centrifugal Clutch

In a centrifugal clutch the torque is transmitted by means of shoes, which slide in radial guides, and make contact through friction surfaces with the inner cylindrical surface of a drum. As the shoes rotate centrifugal force holds them in contact with the drum and allows torque to be transmitted. The shoes are held by springs which just prevent contact until a specified speed of rotation has been reached.

Let n = number of shoes,
   P = centrifugal force on each shoe,
   S = spring force on each shoe,
   μ = coefficient of friction,
   r = radius of friction surface.

   Friction force at each shoe $= \mu \, (P - S)$.

   Friction torque at each shoe $= \mu r \, (P - S)$,

and for n shoes,

   friction torque $= n\mu r \, (P - S)$.   (5.23)

Worked Example

5·5. A centrifugal clutch has four shoes each weighing 2·5 lb and having its centre of gravity at a radius of 2·5 in. The diameter of the friction surface is 6 in. If the clutch is to transmit 10 h.p. at a speed of 1000 rev/min, determine the force which must be exerted by each spring. If the speed of rotation is gradually increased from rest, at what speed will the clutch begin to transmit a torque? Coefficient of friction is 0·35.

SOLUTION

Friction torque $= \dfrac{10 \times 33{,}000}{2\pi \times 1000} = 53$ lb ft.

Radial force required at each shoe $= \dfrac{53 \times 12}{4 \times 0.35 \times 3}$

$= 150$ lb.

Centrifugal force on each shoe at 1000 rev/min

$$= \frac{2.5 \times 105^2 \times 2.5}{386} = 178 \text{ lb.}$$

Required spring force $= 178 - 150 = \mathbf{28}$ **lb.**

Transmission will begin when centrifugal force is equal to spring force, i.e. when

$$\frac{2.5 \times \omega^2 \times 2.5}{386} = 28,$$

i.e.

$$\omega = \sqrt{\left(\frac{28 \times 386}{6.25}\right)} = 41.5 \text{ rad/sec}$$

$= \mathbf{397}$ **rev/min.**

Examples

5.6. The 5 tons load indicated in Fig. 5.10 is raised by means of a wedge. Find the required force P, given that $\tan \theta = 0.2$ and that $\mu = 0.2$ at all rubbing surfaces.

Answer: 3·36 tons.

(L.U. 1944)

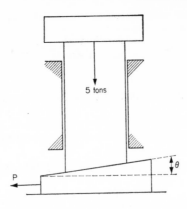

Fig. 5.10. Lifting arrangement for example 5.6

5.7. A turnbuckle with right- and left-hand threads is used to couple two railway coaches. The threads, which are square, have a pitch 0·5 on a mean diameter of 1·5 in. and are of single-start type.

Taking the coefficient of friction as 0·1, find the work to be done in drawing the coaches together a distance of 6 in., (a) against a steady load of 0·25 ton; (b) if the load increases uniformly over the 6 in. from 0·25 to 0·75 ton.

Answer: 2.95 in. tons, 5·90 in. tons.   (L.U. 1946)

5.8. The table of a planing machine is driven at 0·5 ft/sec by a single-start, square-threaded screw of mean diameter 1·75 in. and pitch 0·5 in. The thrust is taken by a ball thrust bearing of negligible friction. Taking the coefficient of friction between the table and bed, and of the screw as 0·15 in each case, determine the horsepower which must be applied to the screw, if the weight of the table is 400 lb and the force due to the tool is 60 lb.

Answer: 0·293 h.p.   (L.U. 1947)

5.9. The cutter of a broaching machine is pulled by a square-threaded screw of 2¾ in. external diameter and ½ in. pitch; the operating nut takes the axial of 90 lb on a flat surface of 3 in. and 4½ in. internal and external diameters respectively. If the coefficient of friction is 0·15 for all contact surfaces on the nut determine the horsepower required to rotate the operating nut when the cutting speed is 25 ft/min.

Answer: 0·47 h.p.   (L.U. 1949)

5.10. A sluice gate, weighing 6 tons, is subjected to a normal pressure of 250 tons. It is raised by means of a vertical screw which engages with a screwed bush fixed to the top of the gate. The screw is rotated by a 50 b.h.p. motor running at a minimum speed of 600 rev/min, a bevel pinion on the motor shaft gearing with a bevel wheel of 80 teeth keyed to the vertical screw. The screw is 5 in. mean diameter and 1 in. pitch. The coefficient of friction for the screw in the nut is 0·08 and between the gate and its guides is 0·10.

If friction losses, additional to those mentioned above, amount to 15 per cent of the total power available, determine the maximum number of teeth for the bevel pinion.

Answer: 14 teeth.

(L.U. 1949)

5.11. A plate clutch consists of a flat driven plate gripped between a driving plate and presser plate so that there are two active driving surfaces each having an inner diameter 8 in. and an outer diameter 14 in. The coefficient of friction is 0·4 and the working pressure is limited to 25 lb/in². Assuming the pressure is uniform, calculate the h.p. which can be transmitted at 1000 rev/min. If the clutch becomes worn so that the intensity of pressure is inversely proportional to the radius, the total axial force on the presser plate remaining unaltered, calculate the h.p. which can now be transmitted at 1000 rev/min and the greatest intensity of pressure on the friction surfaces.

Answer: 185 h.p., 181 h.p., 34·3 lb/in².

(L.U. 1944)

5.12. A friction clutch is required to transmit 45 horsepower at 2000 rev/min. It is to be of single-plate disc type with both sides of the plate effective, the pressure being applied axially by means of springs and limited to 10 lb/in².

If the outer diameter of the plate is to be 12 in., find the required inner diameter of the clutch ring and the total force exerted by the springs. Assume the wear to be uniform and a coefficient of friction of 0·3.

Answer: 8·6 in., 460 lb.

(L.U. 1949)

5.13. A cone clutch has a radii of 5 in. and 6 in. the semi-cone angle being 20°. If the coefficient of friction is 0·25 and the allowable normal pressure is 20 lb/in²., find (a) the necessary axial load; (b) the horsepower that can be transmitted at 1000 rev/min.

Answer: 157 lb, 5·0 h.p.

(L.U. 1947)

5.14. A centrifugal clutch is required to engage at a speed of 500 rev/min and to transmit full load of 10 h.p. at a speed of 1000 rev/min. The clutch has four shoes whose centres of gravity are at a radius of 3 in., the internal diameter of the friction surface being 8 in. If the coefficient of friction is 0·35, determine the required weight of each shoe and the force in each spring.

Answer: 1·76 lb, 37·6 lb.

CHAPTER SIX

BELT DRIVES AND BRAKES

6.1. Flat Belt

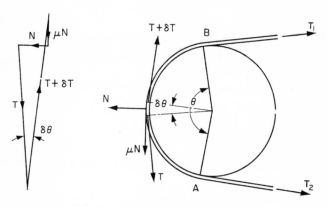

Fig. 6.1. Forces acting on a flat belt

Figure 6.1 shows a flat belt wrapped round the surface of a pulley and making contact over an angle θ. Forces T_1 and T_2 are applied to the ends of the belt so that it is on the point of slipping round the pulley in a clockwise direction. T_1 will clearly be greater than T_2 and the tension in the belt will increase gradually from T_2 at A to T_1 at B.

At any point between A and B let the tension in the belt be T and let it increase by an amount δT in an angle $\delta \theta$. Consider the equilibrium of this small element of the belt.

The forces acting on it are

  (i) the belt tension T and $T + \delta T$,
  (ii) the normal force at the pulley surface N,
  (iii) the friction force μN.

From the force diagram it will be seen that if $\delta\theta$ is very small,

$$\delta T = \mu N \quad \text{and} \quad N = T\delta\theta,$$

hence

$$\delta T = \mu T \delta\theta$$

or

$$\frac{\delta T}{T} = \mu \delta\theta,$$

which, in the limit, as $\delta\theta$ approaches zero, becomes

$$\frac{\mathrm{d}T}{T} = \mu\mathrm{d}\theta.$$

Integrating between the limits T_2 and T_1, and 0 and θ, we have

$$\int_{T_2}^{T_1} \frac{\mathrm{d}T}{T} = \int_0^\theta \mu\mathrm{d}\theta$$

from which

$$\left[\log_e T\right]_{T_2}^{T_1} = \left[\mu\theta\right]_0^\theta,$$

i.e.

$$\log_e \frac{T_1}{T_2} = \mu\theta$$

o

$$\frac{T_1}{T_2} = e^{\mu\theta}. \tag{6.1}$$

6.2. Vee Belt or Rope

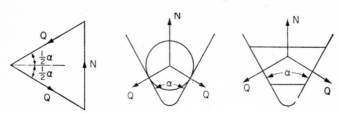

FIG. 6.2. Forces acting on a rope or vee belt

If the pulley has a groove of included angle a and is fitted with a rope or vee belt, the normal reaction at each side of the groove will be Q, whose value, from the force diagram, is given by

$$Q = \tfrac{1}{2}N \cosec \tfrac{1}{2}a.$$

The friction force will be given by

$$2\mu Q = \mu N \cosec \tfrac{1}{2}a.$$

This value now replaces μN in the force diagram of Fig. 6.1, i.e. μ is replaced by $\mu \cosec \tfrac{1}{2}a$.

Thus

$$\frac{T_1}{T_2} = e^{\mu\theta \cosec \frac{1}{2}a}. \tag{6.2}$$

6.3. Centrifugal Tension

If the belt and pulley are rotating with a peripheral speed of v ft/sec, each element of the belt in contact with the pulley will be subjected to a centrifugal force R acting radially outwards as shown in Fig. 6.3. This will produce in the belt an additional tension T_C, whose value may be found from the force diagram shown.

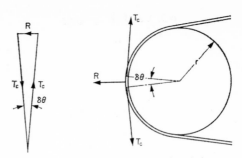

FIG. 6.3. Centrifugal tension in a belt

If, as before, $\mu\theta$ is very small,

$$R = T_C \delta\theta$$

or

$$T_C = R/\delta\theta.$$

Let $w =$ weight of belt per foot run, then the weight of the element will be $wr\delta\theta$ and the centrifugal force on this element will be given by

$$R = \frac{wr\delta\theta}{g} \cdot \frac{v^2}{r} = \frac{wv^2\delta\theta}{g},$$

hence

$$T_C = \frac{R}{\delta\theta} = \frac{wv^2}{g}. \tag{6.3}$$

The total tensions in the two sides of the belt thus become

$$T_1 + \frac{wv^2}{g} \text{ and } T_2 + \frac{wv^2}{g}.$$

The two sides of the belt in which the greater and smaller tensions act are known respectively as the tight side and the slack side.

6.4. Power Transmitted by a Belt

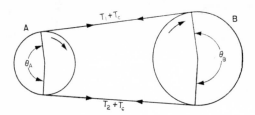

FIG. 6.4. Power transmitted by a belt

Figure 6.4 shows a belt drive in which power is being transmitted from pulley B to pulley A. Since the direction of rotation is clockwise it is clear that the upper side of the belt will be the tight side and the lower the slack side. Since the angle of contact (or angle of lap) on the smaller pulley A is less than on the larger pulley B, slipping will occur on the former with a lower value of the ratio T_1/T_2 than on the latter. This value is, therefore, the one to be used in determining the power which can be transmitted by the drive.

Let v = peripheral velocity of the belt in ft/sec.

The resultant force acting tangentially to either pulley is equal to

$$(T_1 + T_C) - (T_2 + T_C)$$

$$= (T_1 - T_2).$$

Work done per sec $= (T_1 - T_2)\,v$.

$$\text{Power transmitted} = \frac{(T_1 - T_2)\,v}{550}\ \text{h.p.} \qquad (6.4)$$

WORKED EXAMPLE

6.1. 45 h.p. is to be transmitted by an open flat belt drive from a pulley 12 in. in diameter rotating at 1000 rev/min to a second pulley

E

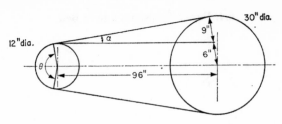

Fig. 6.5.

30 in. in diameter. The distance between the centres of the pulleys is 8 ft. If the weight of the belt material is 0·06 lb/in³, the coefficient of friction is 0·3 and maximum stress in the belt is not to exceed 600 lb/in², determine the required cross-sectional area of the belt.

SOLUTION

Referring to Fig. 6·5,

$$\sin \alpha = \frac{9}{96} = 0\cdot0938, \text{ therefore } \alpha = 5\cdot4°.$$

Therefore angle of lap on smaller pulley

$$\theta = 180° - 2\alpha = 169\cdot2° = 2\cdot95 \text{ rad.}$$

$$\log_e \frac{T_1}{T_2} = 0\cdot3 \times 2\cdot95 = 0\cdot885,$$

$$\frac{T_1}{T_2} = 2\cdot42.$$

Belt speed $v = \dfrac{1000 \times 2\pi \times 1}{60} = 105 \text{ ft/sec.}$

$$T_1 - T_2 = \frac{550 \times 45}{105} = 236 \text{ lb.}$$

Therefore

$$T_1 = \frac{236 \times 2 \cdot 42}{1 \cdot 42} = 402 \text{ lb.}$$

$$T_C = \frac{0 \cdot 06 \times 12A \times 105^2}{32 \cdot 2} = 247A$$

where A = c.s.a. of belt in square inches.

$$T_m = T_1 + T_C,$$

$$600A = 236 + 247A,$$

$$353A = 236,$$

$$A = \mathbf{0 \cdot 67 \text{ in}^2.}$$

6.5. Maximum Power Transmissible

Let T_m = maximum permissible tension in a belt, then the greatest value of $T_1 + T_C = T_m$.

$$T_1 + \frac{wv^2}{g} = T_m,$$

$$T_1 = T_m - \frac{wv^2}{g},$$

therefore

$$T_1 - T_2 = T_1 - \frac{T_1}{e^{\mu\theta}} = \left(T_m - \frac{wv^2}{g}\right)\left(1 - \frac{1}{e^{\mu\theta}}\right)$$

The power transmitted by the belt when it is stressed to its maximum value is given by

$$P = \frac{[T_m - (wv^2/g)]\,[1 - (1/e^{\mu\theta})]}{550}$$

$$= \left(\frac{1 - (1/e^{\mu\theta})}{550} \right) \left(T_m v - \frac{wv^3}{g} \right). \tag{6.5}$$

It will be seen that for a given belt drive the power transmitted is a cubic function of v and will have a maximum value when $(\mathrm{d}P/\mathrm{d}v) = 0$, i.e. when

$$\frac{\mathrm{d}}{\mathrm{d}v} \left(T_m v - \frac{wv^3}{g} \right) = 0,$$

$$T_m - 3 \frac{wv^2}{g} = 0,$$

$$3 \frac{wv^2}{g} = T_m,$$

or

$$T_C = \tfrac{1}{3} T_m. \tag{6.6}$$

Thus maximum possible power is transmitted by a belt drive when the peripheral speed is such that the centrifugal tension is one third of the maximum allowable tension in the belt.

6.6. Initial Belt Tension

In order that a belt shall remain in contact with the pulleys when it is transmitting power it must be assembled with an initial tension T_0.

When transmitting power the tight side will stretch by an amount proportional to the increase in tension $(T_1 + T_C) - T_0$, and the slack side will shorten by an amount proportional to $T_0 - (T_2 + T_C)$. If we assume that the belt remains the same length, then the amount of stretch in the tight side must be equal to the amount of shortening in the slack side, i.e.

$$(T_1 + T_C) - T_0 = T_0 - (T_2 + T_C)$$

or

$$2T_0 = T_1 + T_2 + 2T_C$$

$$T_0 = \frac{T_1 + T_2}{2} + T_C. \tag{6.7}$$

WORKED EXAMPLE

6.2. A vee belt drive is taken from a pulley of effective diameter 6 in., having a groove angle of 50°. The belt has a cross-sectional area of 0·25 in² and is made of material weighing 0·05 lb/in³ and having a safe working stress of 500 lb/in². The angle of lap on the pulley is 165° and the coefficient of friction is 0·35.

Determine the speed of the pulley at which maximum h.p. will be transmitted and the value of this h.p. What must be the initial tension in the belt?

SOLUTION

$$T_m = 500 \times 0·25 = 125 \text{ lb}.$$

For maximum h.p., $T_C = \frac{1}{3}T_m = 42$ lb,

therefore

$$\frac{v^2 \times 0·05 \times 0·25 \times 12}{32·2} = 42.$$

$$v = \sqrt{\left(\frac{42 \times 32·2}{0·15}\right)} = 95·0 \text{ ft/sec}.$$

Speed of pulley $= \dfrac{95 \times 60}{2\pi \times 0·5} = \mathbf{1820 \text{ rev/min}}.$

$$\log_e \frac{T_1}{T_2} = \frac{\mu\theta}{\sin 25°} = \frac{0·35 \times 165\pi}{0·423 \times 180} = 2·38,$$

$$\frac{T_1}{T_2} = 10\cdot 8,$$

$$T_1 = 125 - 42 = 83 \text{ lb},$$

$$T_2 = \frac{83}{10\cdot 8} = 7\cdot 7 \text{ lb}.$$

$$\text{Maximum h.p.} = \frac{(83 - 7\cdot 7) \times 95}{550} = \mathbf{13\cdot 0}.$$

$$\text{Initial tension} = \frac{T_1 + T_2 + 2T_C}{2}$$

$$= \frac{83 + 8 + 84}{2} = \mathbf{88 \text{ lb}}.$$

6.7. Band Brakes

The condition of tension in a belt which is being used as a band brake is the same as in a belt drive, except that since the belt is stationary there will be no centrifugal tension. Slipping takes place between the belt and the drum and the condition of limiting friction holds.

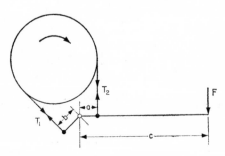

Fig. 6.6. Band brake

The brake is generally applied by means of a lever and it is possible so to arrange the lever that the external force which must be applied is as small as we wish.

Figure 6.6 shows such an arrangement, in which T_1 is the tension in the tight side and T_2 the tension in the slack side.

Taking moments about the fulcrum

$$F \cdot c + T_1 \cdot b = T_2 \cdot a,$$

therefore

$$F = \frac{T_2 a - T_1 b}{c}. \tag{6.8}$$

It will be seen that, whatever may be the actual values of T_1 and T_2, if we make

$$\frac{a}{b} = \frac{T_1}{T_2}$$

the force required to apply the brake will be zero. If a/b is made less than T_1/T_2 then F will be negative, i.e. an upward force must be applied to the lever in order to release the brake and maintain it in this state.

WORKED EXAMPLE

6.3. Figure 6.7 shows a band brake applied to a drum of 16 in. diameter, the angle of lap on the drum being 240°.

If the coefficient of friction between the band and the drum is 0·3, calculate the force P which must be applied to the brake lever in order to exert a braking torque of 200 lb ft when the drum is rotating clockwise.

SOLUTION

$$\log_e \frac{T_1}{T_2} = \frac{0 \cdot 3 \times 240\pi}{180} = 1 \cdot 25,$$

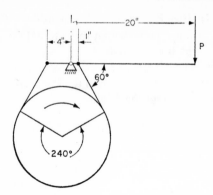

Fig. 6.7. Band brake for worked example 6.3

$$\frac{T_1}{T_2} = 3 \cdot 49,$$

$$T_1 - T_2 = \frac{200 \times 12}{8} = 300 \text{ lb,}$$

$$T_1 = \frac{300 \times 3 \cdot 49}{2 \cdot 49} = 420 \text{ lb,}$$

$$T_2 = 120 \text{ lb.}$$

Taking moments about the fulcrum,
$$P \times 20 + 420 \times \cos 30° = 120 \times 4 \cos 30°,$$

$$P = \frac{60 \cos 30}{20} = \textbf{2·60 lb.}$$

Examples

6.4. In a belt drive the angle of lap on the smaller pulley is 150°. With a belt speed of 4000 ft/min, and a tension in the tight side of the belt of 300 lb, the greatest power which can be transmitted without slip is 13½ h.p. What increase of power would be obtained for the same belt speed and maximum tension by using an idler pulley so as to increase the angle of lap to 210°? Take into account the centrifugal effect, the weight of the belt being $\frac{1}{2}$ lb/ft.

Answer: 3·4 h.p. increase. (L.U. 1940)

6.5. A Vee belt having a lap of 180° has a cross-sectional area of 1 in² and runs in a groove of included angle 45°. The density of the belt is 0·05 lb/in³ and the maximum stress is limited to 600 lb/in², the coefficient of friction being 0·15.

Find the maximum horse-power that can be transmitted if the wheel has a mean diameter of 12 in. and runs at 1000 rev/min.

Answer: 36·1 h.p. (L.U. 1946)

6.6. An open belt connects two flat pulleys. The smaller pulley is 1 ft in diameter and runs at 200 rev/min. The angle of lap on this pulley is 160° and the coefficient of friction between belt and pulley face is 0·25. The belt is on the point of slipping when $3\frac{1}{2}$ h.p. is being transmitted.

Which of the following alternatives would be more effective in increasing the horse-power which could be transmitted:

(a) increasing the initial tension in the belt by 10%;
(b) increasing the coefficient of friction by 10% by the application of a suitable dressing to the belt?

Answer: (a) 10·4%, (b) 9·8% increase. (L.U. 1949)

6.7. An open belt drive connects two pulleys of 48 in. and 20 in. diameter on parallel shafts 12 ft apart. The belt weighs 0·6 lb/ft length, and the maximum tension in it is not to exceed 400 lb. The coefficient of friction is 0·3. The 48 in. pulley which is the driver, runs at 200 rev/min. Due to belt slip on one of the pulleys, the velocity of the driven shaft is only 450 rev/min. Calculate the torque on each of the two shafts, the horsepower transmitted, and the horse-power lost in friction.

What is the efficiency of the drive?

Answer: 412 lb/ft, 172 lb/ft, 93%. (L.U. 1950)

6.8. The band brake indicated in Fig. 6.8 is applied to a shaft carrying a flywheel of 800 lb mass, with a radius of gyration of 18 in., running at 360 rev/min.

Find (a) the torque applied due to a hand load of 20 lb, given that $\mu = 0.2$; (b) the number of turns of the wheel before it is brought to rest.

Answer: 133 lb/in., 552 turns.   (L.U. 1944)

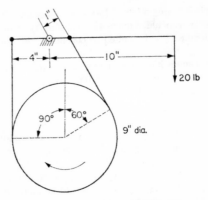

FIG. 6.8. Band brake for example 6.8

CHAPTER SEVEN

STATIC FORCES IN MACHINES

7.1. Introduction

It was stated in the introduction to this book that a machine is used for transmitting energy and the various elements of the machine will therefore be subjected to forces. This chapter will deal with the investigation of forces other than those due to the inertia of the elements.

The static forces in machine elements may be investigated (a) by applying the accepted laws for the equilibrium of forces and couples or (b) by making use of the principle of work.

7.2. Method of Equilibrium of Forces

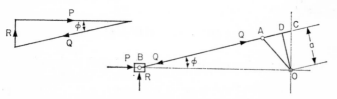

Fig. 7.1. Forces in reciprocating engine mechanism

Figure 7.1. shows the outline of a reciprocating engine mechanism.

P = piston load,
Q = thrust in connecting rod,
R = reaction at crosshead guide or cylinder wall.

If friction is neglected the thrust in the connecting rod will act through the centres of the gudgeon pin and the crank pin, and the reaction at the crosshead will be perpendicular to the line of stroke. The three forces P, Q, R acting at the gudgeon pin will be in equilibrium and the values of Q and R can be found from the force diagram shown.

The turning moment on the crankshaft is given by

$$\text{T.M.} = Q \cdot a. \qquad (7.1)$$

In Fig. 7.1, BA is produced to cut the vertical through O at C and OD is drawn perpendicular to BC.

Comparing the triangle ODC with the force diagram,

$$\text{angle } COD = \phi,$$

$$\text{angle } CDO = \text{a right angle.}$$

Therefore the triangles are similar and

$$\frac{P}{OD} = \frac{Q}{OC},$$

therefore

$$P \times OC = Q \times OD = Q \times a.$$

Thus the turning moment on the crankshaft is given by

$$\text{T.M.} = P \times OC. \qquad (7.2)$$

In the cam mechanism shown in Fig. 7.2, the forces acting at the centre of the roller are

P = resistance to vertically upward motion of follower,

Q = thrust at point of contact of roller and cam,

R = thrust at the follower guide.

If friction is neglected the force Q will act in a direction normal

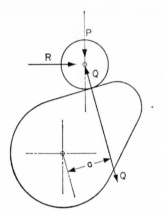

FIG. 7.2. Forces in a cam mechanism

to the cam profile at the point of contact and R will act in a direction perpendicular to P. As in the case of the reciprocating engine the value of Q may be determined by means of a force diagram and the turning moment on the cam will be given by

$$\text{T.M.} = Q \cdot a. \tag{7.3}$$

7.3. Method of Work

This is based on the principle that if no energy is lost (e.g. by friction) then the work output from a machine is equal to the work input.

Referring again to the reciprocating engine mechanism (see

FIG. 7.3. Principle of work applied to reciprocating engine

Fig. 7.3), for any configuration, and knowing the angular velocity of the crank, the velocity of the piston and crosshead can be found by drawing a velocity diagram.

Let P = piston load,

T = resisting torque at crankshaft,

v_B = velocity of crosshead B,

ω = angular velocity of crank OA.

Power input at piston = Pv_B,

Power output at crankshaft = $T\omega$,

hence $T\omega = Pv_B$,

$$T = \frac{Pv_B}{\omega}. \tag{7.4}$$

It is clear that this method may also be used for the case of the cam mechanism discussed above.

Worked Example

7.1. A reciprocating engine has a crank of 8 in. radius and a connecting rod 36 in. long. At the instant when the crank is 45° past i.d.c. the net piston load is 1500 lb. Determine, for this position, the turning moment on the crankshaft, the thrust in the connecting rod and the pressure on the crosshead guide.

Solution

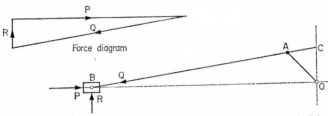

Fig. 7.4. Configuration and force diagram for worked example 7.1

Drawing Fig. 7.4 to scale we find

$$OC = 6{\cdot}55 \text{ in.,}$$

hence turning moment on crankshaft $= 1500 \times 6{\cdot}55 =$ **9830 lb in.**

From the force diagram,
thrust in connecting rod $= Q =$ **1520 lb,**
pressure on guide $= R =$ **239 lb.**

WORKED EXAMPLE

7.2. A symmetrical tangent cam has a base radius of 1 in. and a nose radius of $\frac{1}{2}$ in. as shown in Fig. 7.5, and operates a roller follower of 1 in. diameter whose line of stroke is a straight line offset $\frac{1}{4}$ in. from the axis of rotation of the cam. When the cam is in the position shown in Fig. 7.5 the net vertical load on the follower is 120 lb. Determine the normal thrust between the roller and the side of the cam and the turning moment on the cam shaft.

The diagram may be drawn to scale or values may be calculated.

SOLUTION

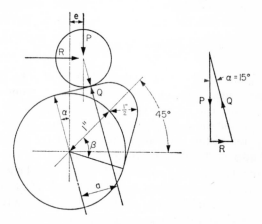

FIG. 7.5. Configuration and force diagram for worked example 7.2

$\cos \beta = 0.5$, therefore, $\beta = 60°$, $a = \beta - 45° = 15°$,

$a = (R + r) \tan 15° + e \cos 15° =$
$$1.5 \times 0.268 + 0.25 \times 0.966 = 0.643 \text{ in.}$$

$Q = P \sec 15° = 120 \times 1.035 = \textbf{124 lb.}$

Turning moment $= 124 \times 0.643 = \textbf{79.7 lb in.}$

7.4. Friction in Link Mechanisms

In dealing with problems concerned with friction in link mechanisms it is convenient to imagine the reaction between the bearing and the journal as acting tangentially to a circle of radius $r \sin \phi$. This circle is known as the friction circle. The use of the friction circle may be illustrated by reference to the reciprocating engine mechanism.

Fig. 7.6. Friction in a reciprocating engine mechanism

Figure 7.6 shows an outline diagram of a horizontal reciprocating engine mechanism with the crank rotating in a clockwise direction. The friction circles, much enlarged for clearness, are shown for the main shaft, the crank pin and the gudgeon pin. P is the piston load, R the reaction at the crosshead guide or cylinder wall, Q the thrust in the connecting rod. The reaction of the main bearing on the shaft will be equal and opposite to Q and the turning moment on the crankshaft will be given by $Q \cdot a$.

The reactions at the bearings will act tangentially to the friction circles so as to oppose the relative motion at the bearings, as shown in Fig. 7.6.

Figure 7.7. shows the mechanism in positions near the dead centres at which the thrust Q in the connecting rod and the reaction at the main bearing act in the same line.

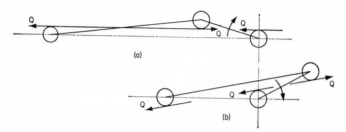

FIG. 7.7. Dead angles in a reciprocating engine mechanism

There will also be similar positions on the other side of the dead centres at which this occurs. Between these two positions at each dead centre the turning moment on the crankshaft will be zero whatever the value of P. The angles between the limiting crank positions are called the "dead angles".

WORKED EXAMPLE

7.3. In the reciprocating engine of example 7.1, the diameters of the main shaft, crank pin and gudgeon pin are respectively 5 in., 4 in. and 3 in., and the coefficient of friction for all rubbing surfaces is 0·06. Determine for the same configuration the turning moment on the crankshaft, the thrust in the connecting rod and the pressure on the guide, taking account of friction.

SOLUTION

Radius of crankshaft friction circle $= 0·06 \times 2·5 = 0·15$ in.
Radius of crank-pin friction circle $= 0·06 \times 2 = 0·12$ in.
Radius of gudgeon-pin friction circle $= 0·06 \times 1·5 = 0·09$ in.
It is clear that if a graphical method were used for this problem,

a very large scale would have to be employed. The solution will
therefore be worked by calculation.

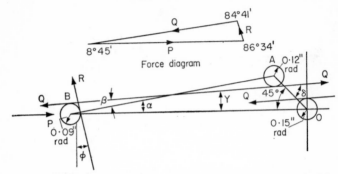

FIG. 7.8. Configuration and force diagram for worked example 7.3

Referring to Fig. 7.8,

$$\sin \alpha = \frac{8 \sin 45°}{36} = \frac{8 \times 0.707}{36} = 0.157,$$

therefore
$$\alpha = 9° 2'.$$

$$\tan \beta = \frac{0.09 + 0.12}{36} = 0.005,$$

therefore
$$\beta = 17'$$

$$\gamma = \alpha - \beta = 8° 45'.$$

$$\tan \phi = 0.06, \quad \text{therefore } \phi = 3° 26'.$$

The angles in the force diagram are therefore as shown and

$$\frac{P}{\sin 84° 41'} = \frac{Q}{\sin 86° 34'} = \frac{R}{\sin 8° 45'},$$

from which

$$Q = \textbf{1519 lb,}$$

$$R = \textbf{229 lb,}$$

$$\delta = 45° + \gamma = 53° 45',$$

$$a = 8 \sin 53° 45' - (0.12 + 0.15) = 6.18 \text{ in.}$$

Therefore

$$\text{Turning moment} = 1519 \times 6.18 = \textbf{9380 lb in.}$$

The above values should be compared with those found in example 7.1.

7.5. Forces in Toothed Gears and Gear Trains

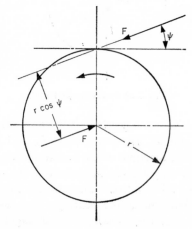

Fig. 7.9. Thrust on gear wheel teeth

Figure 7.9 shows the pitch circle of a toothed gear which is being driven in a counterclockwise direction. The force F acting on the tooth will be inclined to the tangent to the pitch circle at an angle Ψ, the pressure angle. This force will set up an equal and opposite reaction at the centre of the shaft and the two forces will produce a couple which will be equal to the resisting torque in the shaft.

Thus torque $\qquad T = Fr \cos \Psi$

and $\qquad\qquad\qquad F = \dfrac{T}{r \cos \Psi}.$ $\qquad\qquad$ (7.5)

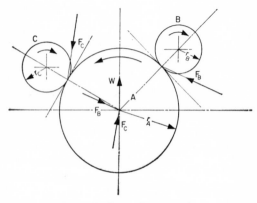

FIG. 7.10. Forces in gear train

In Fig. 7.10 is shown a gear wheel A which is being driven by two pinions B and C. The tooth loads F_B and F_C will set up equal and opposite reactions at the bearings of the shaft carrying the wheel A. The diagram also indicates that the weight W of the wheel A is to be taken into account and the force shown is the corresponding reaction at the bearings. The resultant bearing reaction will be found by drawing a force diagram for the three forces F_B, F_C and W.

WORKED EXAMPLE

7.4. In the double reduction gear shown in Fig. 7.11, the pinion A drives the wheel B, and the pinion C, integral with B, drives the wheel D.

A rotates at 1500 rev/min and transmits 25 h.p. The numbers of teeth in the wheels are: A, 25; B, 60; C, 30; D, 70. All the teeth are of involute shape with a diametrical pitch of 6 and a pressure angle of $20°$. Neglecting the weight of wheels B and C, determine the magnitude and direction of the resultant force on the bearings of wheels B and C and the torque on wheel D.

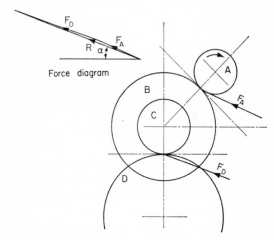

Fig. 7.11. Gear train and force diagram for worked example 7.4

SOLUTION

$$\text{p.c.r. of } A = \frac{25}{2 \times 6} = 2.08 \text{ in.}$$

$$F \cos 20° = \frac{25 \times 33,000 \times 12}{2\pi \times 2.08 \times 1500} = 505 \text{ lb.}$$

$$F_A = \frac{505}{0.94} = 538 \text{ lb.}$$

$$F_D = F_A \times \frac{t_B}{t_C} = 538 \times \frac{60}{30} = 1076 \text{ lb.}$$

Drawing the force diagram to scale we obtain

resultant force $R = 1613$ lb.

$$a = 21 \cdot 6°.$$

Torque on wheel $D = 1076 \cos 20° \times \dfrac{70}{2 \times 6}$

$$= \frac{1076 \times 0 \cdot 94 \times 70}{12} = \textbf{5900 lb in.}$$

7.6. Effect of Friction in Gear Trains

There will be two effects due to friction.

(a) Due to sliding between the teeth the force acting at the tooth profile will be inclined to the tangent to the pitch circle at an angle other than Ψ. This force will be inclined to the line of thrust at an angle Φ, the friction angle. Reference to Fig. 4.2 will show, however, that during the path of approach the true force will be inclined to the pitch circle tangent at an angle $(\Psi + \Phi)$, whilst during the path of recess it will be inclined at an angle $(\Psi - \Phi)$. Further, during some part of the time and possibly during the whole of the time, there will be more than one pair of teeth in contact, with the points of contact in varying positions along the path of contact. It is, therefore, reasonable to assume that on the average the tooth force will be acting along the line of thrust.

(b) Due to friction at the bearings, the reactions on the shaft will be tangential to the friction circle and this will have the effect of reducing the arm of the couple due to each force and thus for a given torque the tooth load will be increased. As a result, although the directions of the forces and their resultant will not be altered, the magnitude of the resultant bearing reaction will be increased.

7.7. Forces and Torques in Epicyclic Gear Trains

In general the external connections to an epicyclic gear are made to the input shaft, the output shaft and one wheel which may be fixed to the casing and held stationary or may be allowed to rotate at a given speed.

Let ω_X, ω_Y and ω_F be the angular velocities of these respective elements and let T_X, T_Y and T_F be the torques applied to them.

It must be made clear that all these quantities are algebraic quantities and may be either positive or negative according to the directions in which they act.

A driving torque will clearly act in the same direction as the angular velocity of the shaft whilst a resisting torque will act in the opposite direction.

Bearing this in mind, and assuming that all elements are rotating with uniform angular velocity, and neglecting any loss due to friction,

(a) the resultant torque will be zero so that

$$T_X + T_Y + T_F = 0, \tag{7.6}$$

(b) the net work done will be zero, and

$$\omega_X T_X + \omega_Y T_Y + \omega_F T_F = 0. \tag{7.7}$$

If the element F is fixed then $\omega_F = 0$ and equation (7.7) becomes

$$\omega_X T_X + \omega_Y T_Y = 0. \tag{7.8}$$

If, due to friction, the power output is η times the power input then the equation will be written

$$\eta \omega_X T_X + \omega_Y T_Y = 0.$$

WORKED EXAMPLE

7.5. In the epicyclic gear shown in Fig. 7.12, X the driving shaft rotates at 500 rev/min and transmits 3 h.p., and the wheel E is fixed.

(a) If the wheel C is allowed to rotate freely determine the torque required to hold the wheel E.

(b) If there is a resisting torque of 30 lb ft applied to the wheel C determine the power transmitted to the shaft Y and the torque required to hold the wheel E.

The numbers of teeth in the wheels are: A, 40; B, 25; C, 90; D, 35; E, 100. Neglect any loss due to friction in the drive.

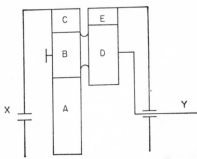

FIG. 7.12. Epicyclic gear train for worked example 7.5

SOLUTION

(a)
$$\frac{N_A - N_Y}{N_E - N_Y} = -\frac{t_E}{t_D} \times \frac{t_B}{t_A},$$

$$\frac{N_X - N_Y}{0 - N_Y} = -\frac{100}{35} \times \frac{25}{40} = -\frac{25}{14},$$

$$14 \times 500 - 14N_Y = 25N_Y,$$

$$N_Y = \frac{14 \times 500}{39} = 180 \text{ rev/min},$$

in the same direction as N_X,

$$T_X = \frac{3 \times 33{,}000}{2\pi \times 500} = 31 \cdot 5 \text{ lb ft.}$$

$$N_X T_X + N_Y T_Y + N_E T_E = 0, \qquad N_E = 0,$$

therefore

$$500 \times 31 \cdot 5 + 180 T_Y = 0,$$

therefore

$$T_Y = -87 \cdot 5 \text{ lb ft.}$$

$$T_X + T_Y + T_E = 0,$$

therefore

$$T_E = -31 \cdot 5 + 87 \cdot 5 = + \mathbf{56 \cdot 0 \text{ lb ft.}}$$

This torque is positive and, therefore, acts in the same direction as the driving torque.

(b)

$$\frac{N_A - N_Y}{N_C - N_Y} = -\frac{t_C}{t_A},$$

$$\frac{500 - 180}{N_C - 180} = -\frac{90}{40},$$

therefore

$$2000 - 720 = -9 N_C + 1620$$

$$N_C = \frac{340}{9} = 37 \cdot 8 \text{ rev/min}$$

in the same direction as N_X.

The resisting torque on this wheel will, therefore, act in the opposite direction, i.e. it will be negative.

Therefore

$$N_X T_X + N_Y T_Y + N_E T_E + N_C T_C = 0, \qquad N_E = 0$$

$$500 \times 31 \cdot 5 + 180 T_Y - 37 \cdot 8 \times 30 = 0$$

$$T_Y = \frac{113 \cdot 1 - 1575}{18} = -\mathbf{81 \cdot 2 \text{ lb ft.}}$$

Power transmitted to $Y = \dfrac{2\pi \times 81 \cdot 2 \times 180}{33,000} = 2 \cdot 78 \text{ h.p.}$

$$T_X + T_Y + T_E + T_C = 0,$$

$$31 \cdot 5 - 81 \cdot 2 + T_E - 30 = 0,$$

$$T_E = 111 \cdot 2 - 31 \cdot 5 = \textbf{79·7 lb ft.}$$

This torque is positive and, therefore, acts in the same direction as the driving torque.

Examples

7.6. In the mechanism shown in example 1.4 the resistance to the motion of the block B is 5 lb and of the slider D is 10 lb.

Determine the value of the turning moment on the crank OA.

Answer: 2·92 lb ft.

7.7. In the shaping machine of example 1.7 the tool load is 100 lb. Calculate the turning moment on the crank O_1A and the maximum bending moment in the link O_2B.

Answer: 370 lb in., 360 lb in.

7.8. The resistance to motion of the follower in the cam mechanism of example 3.9 is 120 lb. Determine for position (*b*) the normal thrust on the cam profile and the turning moment on the cam shaft.

Answer: 120 lb in.

7.9. In the cam mechanism of example 3.6 there is an axial force of 50 lb on the valve at the instant of transition from acceleration to retardation. Determine for this instant, the turning moment on the cam shaft.

Answer: 135 lb in.

7.10. A horizontal reciprocating engine has a crank radius of 6 in. and a connecting rod of length 27 in. At the instant when the crank is 60 deg past i.d.c. the load on the piston is 750 lb. The diameter of the crankshaft and crankpin is 3 in. and of the gudgeon pin is 2 in. The coefficient of friction at all rubbing surfaces is 0·08. Determine (a) neglecting friction and (b) taking friction into account, the turning moment on the crankshaft.

Answer: 4340 lb in., 4130 lb in.

7.11. Two coaxial shafts X and Y are connected by double reduction gearing through a lay shaft Z. The driving shaft X, rotating at 750 rev/min, carries a pinion A (25 teeth) which gears with a wheel B (60 teeth) on the shaft Z. Z also carries a wheel C (20 teeth) which gears with a wheel D (45 teeth) fixed to the shaft Y. The distance between the centres of the shafts is 12 in. If 2 h.p. is being transmitted without loss, determine the magnitude and direction of the resultant force on the bearings of the lay shaft. The teeth are of involute form with a pressure angle of 20 deg.

Answer: 84·0 lb at 47° to the vertical.

7.12. A spur wheel A having 120 teeth of involute form, 20° pressure angle and 6 d.p., is driven by a pinion B (30 teeth) whose axis of rotation is vertically above that of A and by a second pinion C (40 teeth) whose axis of rotation is horizontally to the right of that of A. The wheel A rotates in a clockwise direction at 150 rev/min and 3 h.p. is transmitted by each of the two pinions. Determine the resultant force on the bearings of the wheel A.

Answer: 190 lb at 25° to the vertical.

7.13. In the epicyclic train of example 4.13, X is the driving shaft and transmits 4 h.p. at 200 rev/min. Assuming no losses determine the torque required to hold the fixed wheel for each of the two cases.

Answer: 189 lb ft, 98 lb ft, both in direction of N_X.

7.14. In the epicyclic bevel train of example 4.14, 2 h.p. is being transmitted without loss. Find the torque necessary to fix the wheel D.

Answer: 49 lb ft in the direction of N_G.

7.15. If in the epicyclic gear train of worked example 7.5, the wheel C is fixed and a driving torque of 20 lb ft is applied to the wheel E, the shaft X transmitting the same power at the same speed, find the torque needed to hold the wheel C.

Answer: 56·0 lb ft in the direction of N_X.

CHAPTER EIGHT

INERTIA FORCES IN MACHINES

8.1. Dynamic Equilibrium of a Link

The forces acting on a link of a machine determine its motion and any acceleration it has must be due to the effect of the resultant force or couple. Since a link has inertia, there will be a reaction equal in magnitude and opposite to the accelerating effects. Thus the link can be considered in a state of "dynamic equilibrium" under the action of the accelerating and inertia effects. The dynamic equilibrium may then be investigated by the methods for static equilibrium.

8.2. Inertia of a Link

In some instances the mass of a link can be considered concentrated at a point, e.g. the piston of a reciprocating engine, whilst in others the mass is clearly distributed, e.g. the connecting rod of the engine. Each of these has its characteristic inertia effects as follows:

(a) Inertia due to a concentrated mass

If W is the weight of the link and f its acceleration, then the inertia effect is a force of magnitude $(W \cdot f/g)$ acting, as shown in Fig. 8.1, in a direction opposite to the acceleration.

(b) Inertia due to a distributed mass

The motion of a link AB in a plane consists of the translation of its centre of mass G together with a rotation about the mass

144

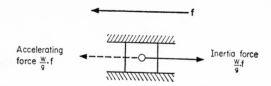

FIG. 8.1. Inertia of a concentrated mass

centre, and these result in an inertia force and couple, as shown in Fig. 8.2.

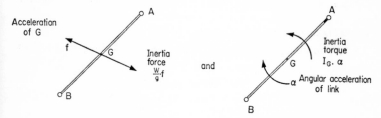

FIG. 8.2. Inertia of a distributed mass

For convenience, these two effects may be considered to arise from a single *equivalent inertia force* of magnitude $(W \cdot f/g)$ acting in the same direction as before but with its line of action a distance x from G, as shown in Fig. 8.3. The equivalent inertia force must provide a turning moment equal to the inertia torque,

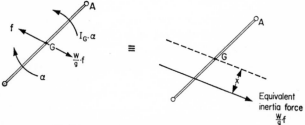

FIG. 8.3. Equivalent inertia force for a link

hence

$$\frac{W}{g} \cdot f \cdot x = I_G \cdot a, \tag{8.1}$$

where I_G is the moment of inertia of the link about G and a its angular acceleration. Thus

$$x = \frac{\text{inertia torque}}{\text{inertia force}} = \frac{I_G \cdot a}{(W/g \cdot f)}. \tag{8.2}$$

The equivalent inertia force may therefore be placed in position on a configuration diagram of the link, or machine, and be included with the other forces in an analysis of the equilibrium.

WORKED EXAMPLE (U.L. 2. EXT. 1952)

    8.1. The crank AB, shown in Fig. 8.4, is 2 ft long and rotates

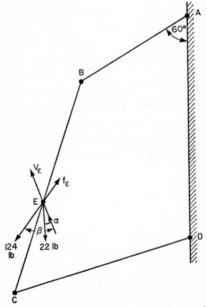

FIG. 8.4. Configuration for worked example 8.1

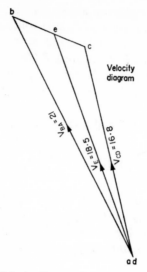

FIG. 8.5. Velocity diagram for worked example 8.1

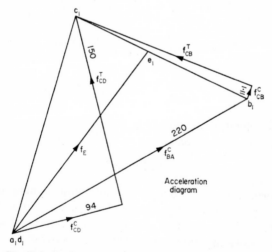

FIG. 8.6. Acceleration diagram for worked example 8.1

in a vertical plane clockwise about A at 100 rev/min. The link CD is 3 ft long and is pivoted freely at D, which is 3 ft 6 in. vertically below A. Link BC is 3 ft 6 in. long and carries a concentrated mass of 22 lb at E, 2 ft from B. When angle $BAD = 60°$ find the velocity and acceleration of E and the turning moment required on the link AB, at this instant, to overcome the weight and inertia of E.

SOLUTION (Chapters 1, 2 and 8 should be understood)

Velocity of B relative to A, $V_{BA} = \dfrac{100 \times 2\pi \times 2}{60} = 21$ ft/sec.

The velocity diagram of Fig. 8.5 is constructed. From this diagram, the velocity of E is given by $ae = \mathbf{18 \cdot 5}$ **ft/sec** in the direction shown on Fig. 8.4. Using the velocity diagram, the necessary centripetal component accelerations can be calculated as follows:

$$f_{BA}^{c} = \frac{V_{BA}^{2}}{BA} = \frac{21^{2}}{2} = 220 \text{ ft/sec}^2 \nearrow$$

$$f_{CB}^{c} = \frac{V_{CB}^{2}}{CB} = \frac{6 \cdot 25^{2}}{3 \cdot 5} = 11 \cdot 1 \text{ ft/sec}^2 \uparrow$$

$$f_{CD}^{c} = \frac{V_{CD}^{2}}{CD} = \frac{16 \cdot 8^{2}}{3} = 94 \text{ ft/sec}^2 \nearrow$$

The acceleration diagram, Fig. 8.6, is then constructed. From this diagram, the acceleration of E is given by vector ae

$$= \mathbf{182} \text{ ft/sec}^2 \nearrow$$

The inertia force at E due to the concentrated mass of 22 lb there $= (22/32 \cdot 2) \times 182 = 124$ lb. This force acts in a direction opposite to the acceleration of E and is shown in Fig. 8.4.

When answering problems involving the inertia of *concentrated masses*, a quick simple solution is often obtained by considering the rates of working (see Chapter 7), and this method will be used here. The lines of action of the forces acting at E are shown in Fig. 8.4.

Rate of working *against* inertia force and weight

$$= 124 \times V_E \cdot \cos\beta + 22 \times V_E \cdot \cos\alpha \text{ ft lb/sec}$$

$$= (124 \times \cos 62° + 22 \times \cos 23°) \, 18{\cdot}5 \text{ ft lb/sec}$$

$$= 1520 \text{ ft lb/sec.}$$

Rate of working on link BA for this = torque on BA × angular velocity of $BA = T \times 10{\cdot}5$ ft lb/sec.

Hence

$$T \times 10{\cdot}5 = 1520, \quad \text{giving } T = \textbf{145 lb.}$$

Worked Example (U.L.2. Int. 1950)

8.2. The connecting rod of an engine weighs 200 lb and is 56 in. long between centres. The centre of gravity is 35 in. from the crosshead centre and the radius of gyration about the centre of gravity is 24 in. The crank is 12 in. long and the engine speed is 240 rev/min. Determine the forces on the crosshead guides (assumed frictionless) and on the crank pin, due to the inertia of the rod when the crank is 45° from the inner dead centre.

Solution

The engine mechanism is shown by AOB in Fig. 8.7, with G the centre of gravity of AB. The linear acceleration of G and the angular acceleration of AB are required so that the equivalent inertia force for AB can be determined. The accelerations will be determined from velocity and acceleration diagrams although an alternative would be to use Klein's construction.

For velocity diagram, Fig. 8.8, $V_{AO} = \dfrac{240}{60} \times 2\pi \times 1 = 25{\cdot}1 \text{ ft/sec.}$

F

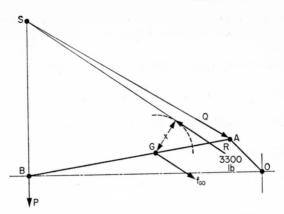

FIG. 8.7. Configuration for worked example 8.2

For acceleration diagram, Fig. 8.9,

$$f^c_{AO} = \frac{V^2_{AO}}{AO} = \frac{25{\cdot}1^2}{1} = 630 \text{ ft/sec}^2,$$

and

$$f^c_{BA} = \frac{V^2_{BA}}{BA} = \frac{18{\cdot}2^2}{56/12} = 71 \text{ ft/sec}^2.$$

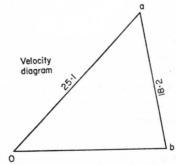

FIG. 8.8. Velocity diagram for worked example 8.2

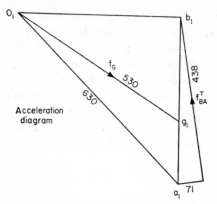

FIG. 8.9. Acceleration diagram for worked example 8.2

From the acceleration diagram, $f_{GO} = o_1 g_1 = 530$ ft/sec^2 in the direction shown in Fig. 8.7.

Inertia force for $AB = \dfrac{200}{32 \cdot 2} \times 530 = 3300$ lb opposite to f_{GO}.

Angular acceleration of $AB = \dfrac{f_{BA}^T}{BA} = \dfrac{438}{56/12} = 94$ rad/sec^2

clockwise.

Inertia torque of $AB = I_G \times 94 = \dfrac{200}{32 \cdot 2} \times \left(\dfrac{24}{12}\right)^2 \times 94$

$$= 2340 \text{ lb ft, anticlockwise.}$$

Position of equivalent inertia force $= 2340/3300 = 0 \cdot 71$ ft from G. The equivalent inertia force is 3300 lb to act across AB in direction opposite to f_{GO} and to produce an inertia torque in an anticlockwise sense. The equivalent inertia force R must act as shown in Fig. 8.7.

At the crosshead B of the engine, the only force acting is at 90°

to the direction of reciprocation since there are no horizontal forces such as friction, gas thrust, inertia of piston. The force acting at *B* is shown in Fig. 8.7 as force *P*. The other forces acting on the connecting rod (weight of rod not included) are the inertia force *R* and a force *Q* at point *A*. Since these three forces must have lines of action that pass through a point, this point is given by the intersection *S* of the two known lines of action. The line of action of the third force *Q* then passes through *S* and *A* and its direction is thus obtained.

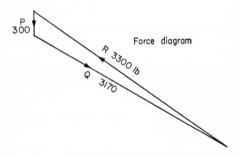

Fig. 8.10. Force diagram for worked example 8.2

The force diagram, Fig. 8.10, can then be drawn to scale and the values and directions of forces *P* and *Q* found, the values being force at *A* = **3170 lb,** force at *B* = **300 lb.**

WORKED EXAMPLE (U.L.2 EXT. 1946)

8.3. The crank *AB* of the linkwork, shown in Fig. 8.11, rotates at a speed of 120 rev/min clockwise. The mass of *BC* is 10 lb and its centre of gravity is 6 in. from *B*. The radius of gyration of *BC* about the centre of gravity is 4·5 in. For the position when *AB* is 60° from the horizontal as indicated, determine the forces acting at the hinges *B* and *C* due to the inertia of *BC*.

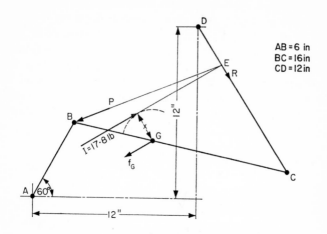

FIG. 8.11. Configuration for worked example 8.3

SOLUTION

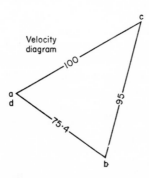

FIG. 8.12. Velocity diagram for worked example 8.3

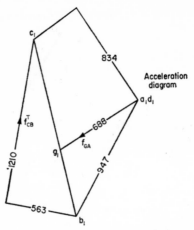

FIG. 8.13. Acceleration diagram for worked example 8.3

For the velocity diagram, $V_{BA} = \dfrac{120}{60} \times 2\pi \times 6 = 75{\cdot}4$ in/sec.

For the acceleration diagram, $f_{BA}^c = \dfrac{V_{BA}^2}{BA} = \dfrac{75{\cdot}4^2}{6} = 947$ in/sec^2;

$$f_{CB}^c = \frac{V_{CB}^2}{CB} = \frac{95^2}{16} = 563 \text{ in/sec}^2;$$

$$f_{CD}^c = \frac{V_{CD}^2}{CD} = \frac{100^2}{12} = 834 \text{ in/sec}^2.$$

The acceleration diagram is then drawn to scale and from it, acceleration of $G = f_G A = 688$ in/sec^2, and therefore the inertia force for $BC = \dfrac{10}{32{\cdot}2} \times \dfrac{688}{12} = 17{\cdot}8$ lb in direction opposite to $f_G A$.

Angular acceleration of $BC = \dfrac{f_{CB}^T}{CB} = \dfrac{1210}{16} = 76$ rad/sec^2 anticlockwise. Equivalent inertia force for $BC = 17{\cdot}8$ lb acting at a distance x from G (Fig. 8.11) opposite to f_G and to give a clockwise turning of link BC.

$$x = \frac{(10/32\cdot2) \times [(4\cdot5/12)]^2 \times 76}{17\cdot8} = 0\cdot186 \text{ ft or } 2\cdot23 \text{ in.}$$

Inertia force I is then positioned on Fig. 8.11, as shown. Forces acting on BC are inertia force I, force R acting at C which must be in direction along CD which has no inertia, and a third force P, which acts at B and passes through point E.

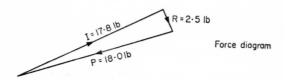

FIG. 8.14. Force diagram for worked example 8.3

The force diagram of Fig. 8.14 can then be drawn giving, by measurement, force at C = **2·5 lb** and force at B = **18 lb.**

Note: Torque on BA would be given by force at B times the perpendicular distance of the line of action of the force from A.

Examples

8.4. The connecting rod for an internal combustion engine has a length between centres of 9 in. and a total weight of 3·25 lb. Its centre of gravity is 6·5 in. from the small end and its radius of gyration about the centre of gravity is 3·75 in., the weight of the piston and gudgeon pin is 4·5 lb, the stroke is 5·5 in. and the cylinder bore is 4 in. Determine the magnitude and direction of the resultant force acting on the crank pin when the crank is at 30° after inner dead centre and its speed is 1600 rev/min if the effective gas pressure is 250 lb/in².

Answer: 1720 lb.

(U.L.2. Ext. 1945)

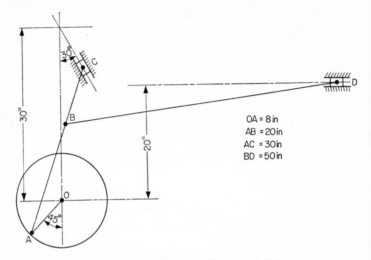

FIG. 8.15. Configuration for example 8.5

8.5. In the mechanism shown in Fig. 8.15, the crank *OA* rotates anticlockwise at 240 rev/min and moves the crosshead *C* in fixed guides by means of the connecting rod *AC*; the crosshead *D* is moved in fixed guides by the rod *BD* pinned to *AC* at *B*. Find the accelerations of *C* and *D* for the position shown. Find also the magnitude and direction of the forces acting on the bar *AC* at *A*, *B* and *C* due to the inertia of a mass of 45 lb at *D* (neglect friction and the weight of all other components). (U.L.1. Ext. 1953)

Answer: 550 ft/sec², 51 ft/sec², *A* = 27 lb, *B* = 72 lb, *C* = 66 lb.

8.6. A valve is operated by a cam which has a base circle diameter of 1·75 in. and a lift of 0·625 in., the cam has tangent flanks and a circular nose and a total angle of action of 120°. The follower which has a roller of 0·75 in. diameter moves along a straight line passing through the cam axis. Find the maximum load to be exerted by the spring to maintain contact between the cam and roller at all times while rotating at 1000 rev/min. The effective weight of valve tappet and spring is 1·25 lb.

Answer: 212 lb.   (U.L.2. Ext. 1949)

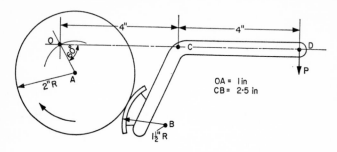

FIG. 8.16. Configuration for example 8.7

8.7. Figure 8.16 shows a circular eccentric of 4 in. diameter rotating about an axis O which is offset 1 in. from the centre of the eccentric. The follower, of weight 0·5 lb, has a radius of gyration of 1·5 in. about its centre of gravity situated at the point C. A vertical force P is applied at D. For a cam speed of 120 rev/min determine the minimum value of P which will ensure contact between the cam and follower when angle $AOC = 60°$. (U.L.2. Ext. 1956)

Answer: 0·0435 lb. (Hint. Identify cam and follower as a four-bar chain).

CHAPTER NINE

TURNING MOMENT DIAGRAMS AND FLYWHEELS

9.1. Torque Variation and Function of a Flywheel

The torque resisting the rotation of the crankshaft of an engine depends upon the load driven by the engine and often this is uniform. The turning moment T developed by the engine, however, can, as shown in Fig. 9.1, vary considerably throughout a cycle. This is due mainly to the changing configuration of the engine mechanism, its inertia and varying gas thrust on the piston.

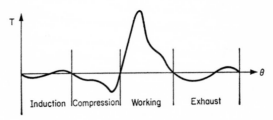

FIG. 9.1. Turning moment diagram

Thus for most positions of the crankshaft there is an unbalanced torque which tends to change the engine speed.

To restrict variations of engine speed throughout a cycle, to narrow limits, a flywheel is fitted to act as a source, or sink, of kinetic energy. A flywheel is chosen as it affords a simple means of absorbing relatively large energies for small speed changes.

9.2. Fluctuation of Energy and Flywheel Duty

If a turning moment diagram be plotted, torque against crank angle, and a curve representing the load torque added, then for any crank position the excess, or deficiency, of torque developed over the load torque is apparent. Also, since the work done by a torque is given by $\int T . d\theta$, the excess of engine energy to be absorbed by a flywheel will be related to the *area* of the portion of the $T-\theta$ diagram cut off by the resisting torque curve; similarly for the energy released by the flywheel. Thus the flywheel size, for a required duty, can be calculated from the fluctuations of energy given by appropriate areas on the $T-\theta$ diagram, above and below the resisting torque curve.

If ΔE is the maximum fluctuation of energy, then the flywheel in changing speed from the lower to the upper limits must absorb that energy. Thus

$$\Delta E = \tfrac{1}{2} \times I . (\omega_1^2 - \omega_2^2), \tag{9.1}$$

where, I is the moment of inertia of the flywheel, and ω_1 and ω_2 are the maximum and minimum angular velocities of the engine and flywheel.

In many cases, because of the cyclic nature of engines, the instantaneous torque can be expressed in terms of series of trigonometrical functions of the crank angle θ. The required flywheel duty may then be determined analytically and without recourse to the practical summation of turning moment diagram areas.

Worked Example (U.L.1. Ext. 1947)

9.1. The turning moment diagram for an engine is drawn on a base of crank angle and the mean resisting torque line added. The areas above and below the mean torque line are $+5\cdot4$; $-1\cdot4$; $+1\cdot6$; $-5\cdot6$ in^2, the scales being 1 in. $\equiv$ 2000 lb ft torque and 1 in. $\equiv 30°$ of crank angle. Find the weight of flywheel required to keep the speed between 297 and 303 rev/min if its radius of gyration is $1\cdot75$ ft.

SOLUTION

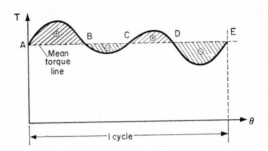

FIG. 9.2. T–θ diagram for worked example 9.1

Figure 9.2 shows the turning moment diagram with the mean torque line cutting the engine torque curve at points A, B, C, D and E. For convenience, let the cycle be such that it starts at A with engine and resisting torques equal. A cycle of events is decided by it occupying a crank angle giving an area of the rectangle below it equal to that below the T–θ curve. Let the energy of the flywheel for a crank position at A be represented by an area e. Then between A and B the additional energy is proportional to the area AB above the mean line. Thus energies are:

$$
\begin{array}{lll}
A & e & = e \qquad \text{minimum} \\
B & e + 5\cdot4 & = e + 5\cdot4 \\
C & e + 5\cdot4 - 1\cdot4 & = e + 3\cdot8 \\
D & e + 5\cdot4 - 1\cdot4 + 1\cdot6 & = e + 5\cdot2 \text{ maximum} \\
E & e + 5\cdot4 - 1\cdot4 + 1\cdot6 - 5\cdot6 & = e \text{ as at } A.
\end{array}
$$

The flywheel has to deal with the maximum fluctuation which will be the largest numerically minus the smallest numerically

$$= (e + 5\cdot6) - (e) = 5\cdot6 \text{ in}^2.$$

But 1 in^2 of diagram represents $2000 \times \pi/6$ ft lb of energy.

Therefore

$$\Delta E = 5{\cdot}6 \times 2000 \times \frac{\pi}{6} = 5870 \text{ ft lb}$$

$$= \frac{I}{2} (\omega_1^2 - \omega_2^2)$$

$$= I \left[\frac{\omega_1 + \omega_2}{2} \right] [\omega_1 - \omega_2].$$

But $\dfrac{\omega_1 + \omega_2}{2}$ = mean angular velocity giving,

$$5870 = I \left(\frac{300}{60} \times 2\pi \right) \left(\frac{6}{60} \times 2\pi \right) \text{ giving,}$$

$$I = \frac{W \cdot k^2}{g} = \frac{5870 \times 60 \times 60}{300 \times 6 \times 2\pi \times 2\pi},$$

hence if $k = 1{\cdot}75$ ft, $W = \textbf{3120 lb.}$

WORKED EXAMPLE (U.L.1. EXT. 1955)

9.2. For a four-cylinder petrol engine the graph of crankshaft torque against crank angle may be represented by straight lines extending between the following points:

Crank angle in degrees	0	20	50	180
Torque in lb ft	0	200	200	0

The sequence is repeated every half-revolution, and the mean speed of the engine is 620 rev/min.

Determine the weight of the flywheel having a radius of gyration of 11 in. which must be fitted in order to restrict the variation of speed to $\pm 0{\cdot}5$ per cent of the mean speed when the engine is driving a machine exerting a constant resisting torque.

SOLUTION

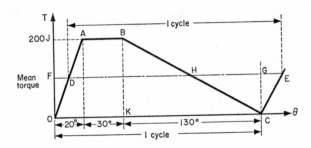

FIG. 9.3. T–θ diagram for worked example 9.2

The turning moment diagram $OABC$ is shown in Fig. 9.3. If one cycle extends over 0° to 180° then the area under the mean torque line must equal that under the curve $OABC$. Thus,

$$T_{\text{mean}} \times 180 = (\tfrac{1}{2} \times 200 \times 20) + (200 \times 30) + (\tfrac{1}{2} \times 200 \times 130),$$

$$T_{\text{mean}} = 116\cdot7 \text{ lb ft.}$$

The mean torque line $FDHGE$ is shown cutting the T–θ curve at points D, H, E, etc.

Since areas cut off above and below the mean torque line will enable fluctuations of energy to be calculated, *the cycle* may be selected to make these calculations as simple as possible. Let the cycle, occupying 180°, be from the crank angle corresponding to D to that corresponding to E as shown. Then there is *one* area above and *one* area below the mean line. Either of these areas, $DABH$ or HCE, will equal the maximum fluctuation of energy. From similar triangles,

$$GE = FD = 116\cdot7 \times \frac{20}{200} = 11\cdot67°,$$

$$HG = 116\cdot7 \times \frac{130}{200} = 75\cdot8°.$$

Area of triangle $CHE = \frac{1}{2}(116 \cdot 7 + 75 \cdot 8) \, 116 \cdot 7$ ft lb degrees, or

fluctuation of energy $\Delta E = \frac{1}{2} \times 116 \cdot 7 \times 86 \cdot 47 \times \dfrac{\pi}{180}$ ft lb.

$$E = 89 \text{ ft lb.}$$

Thus, for the flywheel,

$$89 = \tfrac{1}{2} \cdot I \, (\omega_1^2 - \omega_2^2) = I \cdot \omega \, (\omega_1 - \omega_2).$$

But

$$\omega_1 - \omega_2 = 2 \times 0 \cdot 5\% \text{ of } \omega = \frac{I}{100} \times \omega.$$

Therefore

$$89 = \frac{I}{100} \times \omega^2 = \frac{I}{100} \times \left(\frac{620}{60} \times 2\pi \right)^2$$

and

$$I = \frac{89 \times 100 \times 60 \times 60}{620 \times 620 \times 2\pi \times 2\pi} = 2 \cdot 11 \text{ slugs . ft}^2,$$

$$W = \frac{I \cdot g}{k^2} = \frac{2 \cdot 11 \times 32 \cdot 2}{(11/12)^2} = \textbf{81 lb.}$$

WORKED EXAMPLE (U.L.1. EXT. 1954. (part (a) only))

9.3. The torque exerted by a multicylinder engine running at a mean speed of 240 rev/min against a uniform resistance is T lb ft $= 2500 + 4000 \sin \theta + 600 \sin 2\theta + 60 \sin 3\theta$.

Find the horsepower of the engine and the minimum weight of the flywheel if its radius of gyration is 36 in. and the maximum fluctuation of speed is to be $\pm 1\%$ of the mean.

SOLUTION

The engine torque consists of a constant portion $= 2500$ lb ft together with a portion $4000 \sin\theta + 600 \sin 2\theta + 60 \sin 3\theta$ which has different values depending on the value of θ. A "cycle"

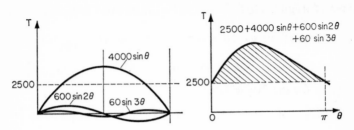

Fig. 9.4. T–θ diagram for worked example 9.3

will be such that, over it, the trigonometrical portion of the torque gives a total energy of zero, otherwise there would be a surplus or deficiency of energy and events would not repeat. Thus, *without any calculations*, it can be seen by inspection that the mean torque = 2500 lb ft. Figure 9.4 shows the torque components sketched separately and combined to give the resultant torque.

$$\text{Horsepower} = \frac{\text{mean torque} \times \text{angular velocity}}{550}$$

$$= 2500 \times \frac{240}{60} \times 2\pi \times \frac{1}{550} = \textbf{114 h.p.}$$

Since there will be one area above and one area below the mean line, areas shown shaded in Fig. 9.4, then maximum fluctuation of energy will be given by the area either above or below. Thus

$$\Delta E = \int_0^\pi (4000\sin\theta + 600\sin 2\theta + 60\sin 3\theta)\, \mathrm{d}\theta$$

giving

$$\Delta E = 8040 \text{ ft lb} = \tfrac{1}{2} \cdot I\left(\omega_1^2 - \omega_2^2\right)$$

or

$$8040 = I \cdot \omega \cdot \frac{2}{100} \cdot \omega,$$

and thus

$$I = \frac{8040 \times 100}{2 \times (8\pi)^2} = 637 \text{ slugs ft.}$$

$$W = \frac{637 \times 32 \cdot 2}{9} = \mathbf{2280 \ lb.}$$

WORKED EXAMPLE (U.L.1 EXT. 1941)

9.4. An engine has three single acting cylinders, the cranks being spaced at 120° to each other. The crank effort diagram for each cylinder consists of a triangle having the following values:

Angle	0	60°	180°	180° to 360°	
Torque	0	150 (max)	0	0	lb ft.

Find: (a) the mean torque,

(b) the moment of inertia of the flywheel in lb ft² to keep the speed within 180 ± 3 rev/min

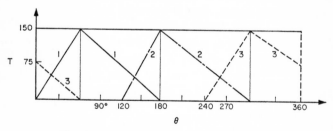

FIG. 9.5. T–θ diagram for worked example 9.4

SOLUTION

(a) Figure 9.5 shows the separate diagrams for the three cylinders each displaced by 120° and therefore part of that for cylinder 3 will appear, over a 0–360° range, at the beginning of the range.

Over 360° the total area under the resultant T–θ diagram would be 3 times that for one cylinder, thus,

$$T_{\text{mean}} \times 360 = 3 \times \tfrac{1}{2} \times 150 \times 180,$$
$$T_{\text{mean}} = \textbf{112·5 lb ft.}$$

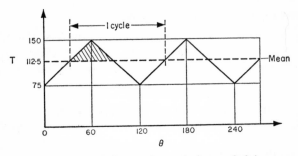

FIG. 9.6. T–θ diagram for worked example 9.4

(b) The T–θ curves for the separate cylinders are combined into a single resultant T–θ diagram, as shown in Fig. 9.6. (Note the sum of three straight lines is a straight line.)

The mean torque line is added. Each *cycle* occupies 120° and a convenient one to consider is that shown in Fig. 9.6. The maximum fluctuation of area is a triangle shown shaded. The base of the triangle is 60° and its height is $37\frac{1}{2}$ lb ft. Hence fluctuation of energy $\Delta E = \tfrac{1}{2} \times 37\frac{1}{2} \times 60 \times \pi/180$ ft lb.

$$= 19\cdot65 \text{ ft lb.}$$

$$19\cdot65 = I \times \omega(\omega_1 - \omega_2) = I \times \frac{180}{60} \times 2\pi \times \frac{6}{60} \times 2\pi,$$

$$I = \frac{19\cdot65 \times 60 \times 60}{180 \times 6 \times 2\pi \times 2\pi} = 1\cdot66 \text{ slugs ft}^2 \text{ or,}$$

$$= 1\cdot66 \times 32\cdot2 = \textbf{53·3 lb ft}^2.$$

Examples

9.5. The turning moment diagram for a multicylinder engine has been drawn to a scale of, 1 in. $\equiv 5000$ lb ft vertically, and 1 in. $\equiv 30°$ horizontally, the intercepted areas between output torque curve and mean resistance line, taken in order, are: -0.52; $+1.24$; -0.92; $+1.4$; -0.85; $+0.72$; -1.07 in². when the engine is running at 800 rev/min.

If the weight of the flywheel is 1200 lb, and the total fluctuation from maximum to minimum speed does not exceed 2 per cent of the mean speed, what is the minimum value of the radius of gyration?

Answer: 0·93 ft.

(U.L.1. Ext. 1948)

9.6. The turning moment diagram of a single-cylinder double acting engine may be taken as two triangles each having a base of 180°. The maximum torques are 6000 lb ft, and 4600 lb ft. The crank rotates at an average speed of 120 rev/min, the resisting torque being constant. The radius of gyration of the flywheel is $3\frac{1}{2}$ ft.

Find (a) the average horsepower of the engine; (b) the weight of flywheel necessary to limit the total speed fluctuation to 3 per cent of the mean speed.

Answer: (a) 60·5 h.p.; (b) 1631 lb.

(U.L.1. Int. 1952)

9.7. The value of the turning moment exerted by a multicylinder engine, where θ is a crank angle, is given by $12,250 -6000\sin\theta +1500\sin3\theta$ lb ft.

Find the radius of gyration of the flywheel, whose weight is $1\frac{1}{4}$ tons, if the variation in speed is not to exceed $\pm 1\frac{1}{4}$ per cent of the mean speed of 250 rev/min.

Explain a method by which you may determine the angular position of the flywheel relative to one rotating at a constant speed of 250 rev/min.

Answer: 2·71 ft.

(U.L.2. Ext. 1948)

9.8. A rolling mill is to be driven by an electric motor giving a steady output of 200 h.p., independent of speed. A heavy flywheel is directly coupled to the motor to take peak loads and is in the form of a solid disc of cast iron 10 in. thick. During a particular period of $9\frac{1}{2}$ sec, the power absorbed by the mill is 500 h.p. for 2 sec, 80 h.p. for 4 sec and 400 h.p. for $3\frac{1}{2}$ sec.

Find the minimum diameter of flywheel required if the speed is allowed to fall, during the $9\frac{1}{2}$ sec, from 500 to 450 rev/min. Ignore the inertia of the motor armature and mill and take the weight of cast iron as 0·25 lb/in³.

Answer: 6·3 ft.

(U.L.1. Ext. 1954)

9.9. The equation of the turning moment curve of a three-crank engine is $M = 14,000 + 4665\sin3\theta$ lb ft, where θ is the crank angle in radians. The moment of inertia of the flywheel is 4·5 tons ft², and the mean engine speed is 300 rev/min. Calculate:

(a) the horsepower of the engine,

(b) the total percentage fluctuation of speed of the flywheel,

    (i) if the resisting torque is constant

    (ii) if the resisting torque is $14,000 + 2000\sin\theta$ lb ft.

Answer: (a) 800 h.p.; (b) (i) 1·01; (ii) 1·58 per cent.   (U.L.2. Ext. 1956)

9.10. An air compressor has three single acting cylinders. The crankshaft has three cranks, set at angular intervals of 120°.

The torque required by each crank increases uniformly from zero to 600 lb ft as the crank rotates 150° from the outer dead centre position, and then diminishes uniformly to zero during the next 30°. During the remaining 180° of crank rotation the torque is zero.

(a) Plot to scale the combined torque diagram for the three cranks.

(b) A flywheel attached to the crankshaft restricts the total speed variation to 5 per cent of the mean speed. Assuming that the driving torque is constant, find the mean kinetic energy of the flywheel.

Answer: (b) 1200 ft lb.   (U.L.1. Int. 1949)

CHAPTER TEN

ENGINE GOVERNORS

THE purpose of an engine governor is to control the quality, or quantity, of fuel supplied so that the power generated may suit the demands and thus help to maintain the engine speed constant. Most modern governors are of the spring centrifugal, or inertia, type.

10.1. Spring-controlled Centrifugal Governor

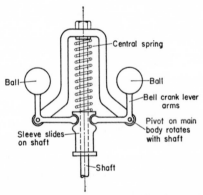

FIG. 10.1. Spring-controlled centrifugal governor

The governor shaft, shown in Fig. 10.1, is rotated by the engine and a sleeve carried on the shaft is positioned by the bell crank lever. The position taken by the sleeve is due mainly to the effect of the resultant moment of the centrifugal forces on the balls,

and the central force of the spring. The fuel supply is controlled
by the sleeve movement.

The dynamic characteristics of the governor may be conveniently
considered by reference, as in the following paragraph, to a control
force diagram.

10.2. Controlling Force and Diagram

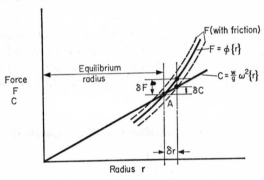

FIG. 10.2. Control force diagram

The centrifugal force C acting on a ball, due to its motion
in a circular path of radius r, is resisted by a radially inwards
control force F. The control force arises from the compression,
or extension, of a control spring, the weight of the sleeve, lever
arms and balls together with frictional effects. The control force
will therefore be a function of the sleeve and ball position for a
given governor, i.e. a function of the ball radius of rotation. A
curve showing the relationship between F and r is called a control
force diagram, as shown in Fig. 10.2.

10.3. Equilibrium, Stability and Isochronism

The terms are most easily considered by referring to the control
force diagram of Fig. 10.2.

(a) *Equilibrium.* The governor will be in equilibrium when, for each ball, the control force F acting on it is equal and opposite to the centrifugal force C. The centrifugal force is given by

$$C = \frac{w}{g} \cdot \omega^2 \cdot r, \tag{10.1}$$

where w is the weight of a ball and ω is the angular velocity in the circular path of radius r. Thus for a given speed of rotation, C is proportional to r and the centrifugal force curve plotted on a control force diagram will be a straight line, as shown in Fig. 10.2.

The radius of rotation for which the governor is in equilibrium is then given by the intersection of the centrifugal and control force curves.

(b) *Stability.* This refers to the behaviour of the governor following a slight disturbance when rotating at constant speed. Let the radius of rotation increase δr as shown in Fig. 10.2. Provided the change in F is greater than the change in C the balls will return to their equilibrium position. Thus for a governor to be stable the slope of the control force curve must be greater than the slope of the centrifugal force line; similarly for a decrease in radius giving for stability,

$$\frac{\mathrm{d}F}{\mathrm{d}r} > \frac{\mathrm{d}C}{\mathrm{d}r},$$

i.e.

$$\frac{\mathrm{d}F}{\mathrm{d}r} > \frac{w}{g} \cdot \omega^2. \tag{10.2}$$

(c) *Isochronism.* A state of equilibrium that exists when the slope of the control force curve is the same as that of the centrifugal force line is such that the balls, if slightly displaced, will move rapidly out, or in, to their extreme positions. The governor is then said to be isochronous, and behaves as though it had infinite sensitiveness.

(*d*) *Effect of sleeve friction.* Under ideal conditions, the control force curve would be plotted allowing for frictional forces and since these oppose relative motion, there would be a control force curve for increase of speed, i.e. increase of ball radius, and a different curve for decrease of speed. These curves are shown dotted in Fig. 10.2.

Thus there are *two* equilibrium speeds for each ball position. Care must therefore be taken when considering isochronism as, for example, a spring governor designed to operate near the isochronous condition ignoring sleeve friction, could in practice be stable only when the speed is falling.

10.4. Isochronism of a Spring-controlled Governor

Ignoring friction, a spring-controlled governor is usually considered to have a straight line control curve and for isochronism this line must coincide with the centrifugal force line which must pass through the origin. An existing governor may therefore be made isochronous by,

(i) changing the spring stiffness to alter the slope of the control curve, as shown in Fig. 10.3(a), or

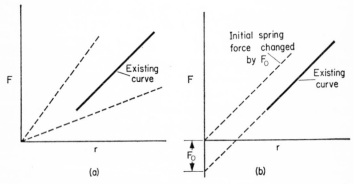

Fig. 10.3. Control force diagrams for isochronism

(ii) by changing the initial spring force to displace the control curve to pass through the origin without, as shown in Fig. 10.3(b), altering its slope.

Worked Example (U.L.2. Ext. 1950)

10.1. A governor of the Hartnell type, having the dimensions shown in Fig. 10.4, runs at a mean speed of 300 rev/min; each ball weighs 5 lb and a 3 per cent speed reduction causes a sleeve movement of $\frac{1}{4}$ in. If the ball arm is vertical at the mean speed and

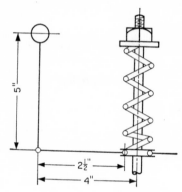

Fig. 10.4. Governor of worked example 10.1

gravitational effects may be ignored, determine the spring stiffness in lb/in. Neglect the weight of the arms. By how much must the adjusting nut be screwed down to render the governor isochronous and what will be the resulting operational speed of the governor?

Solution

Control force for 4 in. radius $= \dfrac{5}{32\cdot5} \times \dfrac{4}{12} \left(\dfrac{300}{60} \times 2\pi\right)^2 = 51$ lb.

If the sleeve moves down $\frac{1}{4}$ in., the balls move in $\frac{1}{2}$ in. and new radius = 3·5 in. with a control force equal to

$$\frac{5}{32 \cdot 5} \times \frac{3 \cdot 5}{12} \left(\frac{291}{60} \times 2\pi\right)^2 = 42 \text{ lb at a new speed of 291 rev/min}$$

Hence the difference in force at each ball = $51 - 42 = 9$ lb. Moments about pivot give an equivalent force at the sleeve equal to

$$9 \times \frac{5}{2\frac{1}{2}} = 18 \text{ lb for each ball.}$$

Total load change at spring for $\frac{1}{4}$ in. extension = $2 \times 18 = 36$ lb.

Therefore stiffness $= \dfrac{36}{\frac{1}{4}} = \mathbf{144 \ lb/in.}$

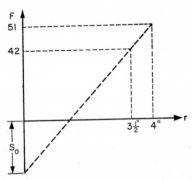

FIG. 10.5. Control force diagram of worked example 10.1

Figure 10.5 shows the control force curve and for isochronism this curve must pass through the origin and have a slope of

$$\frac{51 - 42}{\frac{1}{2}} = 18 \text{ lb/in.}$$

Thus initial spring force must be increased by an amount S_0, where $S_0 = 4 \times 18 - 51 = 21$ lb for each ball, or 42 lb total.

Compression of spring for this $= \dfrac{42 \times 2}{144} = $ **0·583** in. at the spring.

Slope of control force curve $= \dfrac{\mathrm{d}F}{\mathrm{d}r} = \dfrac{w}{g} \cdot \omega^2 = 18 \times 12$ lb/ft.

Thus

$$\omega^2 = \frac{18 \times 12 \times 32 \cdot 2}{5} = 1390$$

$$\omega = 37 \cdot 3 \text{ rad/sec or } N = \textbf{357 rev/min}$$

WORKED EXAMPLE (U.L.1. EXT. 1945)

10.2. A spring-loaded governor of the Hartnell type has arms of equal length. The weights rotate in a circle of $6\frac{1}{2}$ in. diameter when the sleeve is in mid-position and the weight arms are vertical. The equilibrium speed for this position is 450 rev/min neglecting friction. The maximum sleeve movement is to be $1\frac{1}{4}$ in. and the

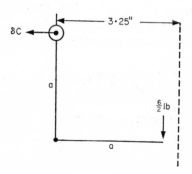

FIG. 10.6. Governor of worked example 10.2

maximum variation of speed (allowing for friction) is to be ± 5 per cent of the mid-position speed. The weight at the sleeve is $7\frac{1}{2}$ lb and friction may be considered equivalent to 6 lb at the sleeve. The power of the governor must be sufficient to overcome the friction by a 1 per cent change of speed at mid-position. Determine the weight of each rotating mass, the spring stiffness in lb/in. and the initial compression of the spring.

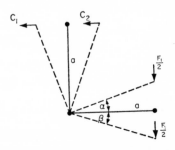

Fig. 10.7. Governor of worked example 10.2

Solution

The weight w of each ball has to be of such a value that, when in the mid-position shown in Fig. 10.6, the change in centrifugal force is balanced against the frictional force. Change in centrifugal force due to increase of speed of 1 per cent

$$= \delta C = \frac{w}{32 \cdot 2} \times \frac{3 \cdot 25}{12} \left(\frac{450}{60} \times 2\pi \right)^2 (1 \cdot 01^2 - 1^2) = 0 \cdot 373w \text{ lb for each.}$$

Moments about the pivot give $0 \cdot 373w \times a = 6/2 \times a$ and

$$w = \mathbf{8 \cdot 05 \ lb.}$$

Figure 10.7 shows the forces and arm positions at top and bottom speeds. The radii of rotation and corresponding speeds are, 3·875 in. and 472·5 rev/min, 2·625 in. and 427·5 rev/min.

For top speed, moments about pivot,

$$\frac{8\cdot05}{32\cdot2} \times \frac{3\cdot875}{12}\left(\frac{472\cdot5}{60} \times 2\pi\right)^2 \times a\cos\alpha = \frac{F_1}{2} \times a\cos\alpha \text{ giving}$$

$$F_1 = 397 \text{ lb.}$$

For bottom speed, moments about the pivot,

$$\frac{8\cdot05}{32\cdot2} \times \frac{2\cdot625}{12}\left(\frac{472\cdot5}{60} \times 2\pi\right)^2 \times a\cos\beta = \frac{F_2}{2} \times a\cos\beta \text{ giving}$$

$$F_2 = 220 \text{ lb.}$$

If S_1 and S_2 are the spring forces at the sleeve, then

$$F_1 = S_1 + \text{friction} + \text{sleeve weight giving}$$
$$S_1 = 397 - 6 - 7\tfrac{1}{2} = 383\cdot5 \text{ lb}$$

and

$$F_2 = S_2 - \text{friction} + \text{sleeve weight giving}$$
$$S_2 = 220 + 6 - 7\tfrac{1}{2} = 218\cdot5 \text{ lb.}$$

Thus

$$S_1 - S_2 = 165 \text{ lb and so the spring stiffness}$$

$$= \frac{165}{1\cdot25} = \textbf{132 lb/in.}$$

The initial compression (taken as sufficient to give position for lowest speed) $= \dfrac{S_2}{132} = \textbf{1·66 in.}$

WORKED EXAMPLE (U.L.2. EXT. 1943)

10.3. Part of a spring-controlled governor is shown in Fig. 10.8. The bell crank levers carried by a rotating casing each have a ball arm 4 in. long and a sleeve arm 5 in. long. When the sleeve is in its mid-position, the ball arms are vertical, the sleeve arms are horizontal, and the radius of the ball path is 6 in. The balls each weigh 8 lb and each is controlled by a helical spring as shown. The stiffness of each spring is 60 lb/in. and is initially compressed 2 in. for the bottom position of the sleeve. If the sleeve lifts $\frac{1}{2}$ in. from its bottom to mid-position, determine the operating speeds for these two positions.

The balls, when in the mid-position and rotating at the equilibrium speed, are given a small outward displacement. Calculate the resulting frequency of free vibration of the balls.

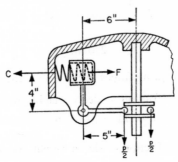

FIG. 10.8. Governor of worked example 10.3

SOLUTION

At mid-position (angular velocity ω_1) the centrifugal force C_1

$$= \frac{8}{32 \cdot 2} \times \frac{6}{12} \times \omega_1^2.$$

Compression of spring $= 2 + \frac{4}{5} \times 0 \cdot 5 = 2 \cdot 04$ in.

Spring force $= 60 \times 2 \cdot 04 = 144$ lb $= F_1$.

Sleeve force $= \frac{P}{2} = 10$ lb.

Moments of these forces about the pivot give,

$$4(C_1 - F_1) = \frac{5P}{2} \quad \text{or} \quad \frac{8 \times 6 \times \omega_1^2}{32 \cdot 2 \times 12} = 12 \cdot 5 + 144 = 156 \cdot 5$$

and hence $\omega_1^2 = 1260$, $\omega_1 = 35 \cdot 4$ rad/sec or $N_1 = 338$ rev/min. *At bottom position* (angular velocity ω_2) the radius of rotation

$$= 6 - \frac{4}{5} \times 0 \cdot 5 = 5 \cdot 6 \text{ in.}$$

Moments of forces about the pivot give

$$\frac{8}{32 \cdot 2} \times \frac{5 \cdot 6}{12} \times \omega_2^2 = 12 \cdot 5 + 120 \text{ giving } \omega_2^2 = 1140$$

$$\omega_2 = 33 \cdot 7 \text{ rad/sec or } N_2 = 323 \text{ rev/min.}$$

Let the balls have their radii of rotation increased by δr, then resultant change of forces on a ball

$$= \frac{w}{g} \cdot \omega_1^2 \cdot \delta r - 60 \times 12 \cdot \delta r.$$

Resultant torque on arm

$$= \frac{4}{12} \left\{ \frac{8}{32 \cdot 2} \times 1260 \right\} \delta r - 60 \times 12 \times \frac{4}{12} \times \delta r$$

$$= -136 \times \delta r \text{ lb ft} = T.$$

Equation of motion is $I \cdot \dfrac{\mathrm{d}^2\theta}{\mathrm{d}t^2} + T = 0$ giving

$$\left\{ \frac{8}{32 \cdot 2} \times \left(\frac{4}{12} \right)^2 + \frac{10}{32 \cdot 2} \times \left(\frac{5}{12} \right)^2 \right\} \frac{\mathrm{d}^2\theta}{\mathrm{d}t^2} + 136 \times \frac{4}{12} \cdot \delta\theta = 0$$

giving $\omega_N^2 = \dfrac{\text{angular acceleration}}{\text{angular displacement}} = \dfrac{45\cdot3 \times 32\cdot2 \times 144}{(8 \times 16) + (10 \times 25)}$

and $\omega_N = 23\cdot2$ and the frequency of vibration $= \dfrac{\omega_N}{2\pi} \times 60$

$$= \mathbf{222\ vib/min.}$$

WORKED EXAMPLE (U.L.2. EXT. 1948)

10.4. The centrifugal governor shown in Fig. 10.9 has two operating masses each of weight W lb carried at the ends of bell crank levers; the masses are connected directly to one another by two close coiled helical springs. In the position shown, with the weight arms parallel to the axis of rotation, the equilibrium speed

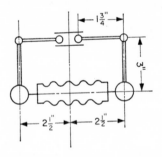

FIG. 10.9. Governor of worked example 10.4

is 850 rev/min. Find (a) the value of W if, when the speed is increased by 1 per cent without any change of radius from the given position, an axial force of $5\frac{1}{4}$ lb is required at the sleeve to maintain equilibrium; (b) the strength and extension of the spring if the rate of sleeve movement when in the mid-position is 1 in. per 600 rev/min change of speed.

SOLUTION

(a) Equilibrium speed $= \dfrac{850}{60} \times 2\pi = 89 \cdot 1$ rad/sec.

Change in centrifugal force per mass due to 1 per cent speed change

$$= \frac{W}{32 \cdot 2} \times \frac{2 \cdot 5}{12} \times 89 \cdot 1^2 \, (1 \cdot 01^2 - 1) \text{ lb.}$$

Moments about pivot

$$\frac{W}{32 \cdot 2} \times \frac{2 \cdot 5}{12} \times 89 \cdot 1^2 \, (1 \cdot 01^2 - 1) \times 3 = \frac{5 \cdot 25}{2} \times 1 \cdot 75,$$

hence $W = \textbf{1·49 lb.}$

(b) Change in control force = change in centrifugal force which can arise due to changes of speed and radius of rotation, thus

$$\frac{\mathrm{d}F}{\mathrm{d}r} = \frac{W}{g} \cdot \frac{\mathrm{d}}{\mathrm{d}r} \, (r \cdot \omega^2) = \frac{W}{g} \left\{ \omega^2 + 2\omega \cdot r \cdot \frac{\mathrm{d}\omega}{\mathrm{d}r} \right\}.$$

But $\omega = 89 \cdot 1$, $r = 2\frac{1}{2}$ in. If sleeve moves 1 in. then the change in r

$$= 1 \times \frac{3}{1 \cdot 75} \text{ in.} \quad \text{and} \quad \mathrm{d}\omega = \frac{600}{60} \times 2\pi = 20\pi \text{ rad/sec.}$$

Thus $\dfrac{\mathrm{d}\omega}{\mathrm{d}r} = 20\pi \times \dfrac{1 \cdot 75}{3 \times 1}$ rad/sec/in.

and

$$\frac{\mathrm{d}F}{\mathrm{d}r} = \frac{1 \cdot 49}{32 \cdot 2 \times 12} \left\{ 89 \cdot 1^2 + 2 \times 89 \cdot 1 \times 2 \cdot 5 \times 20\pi \times \frac{1.75}{3} \right\}$$

$$= \textbf{93·7 lb/in.}$$

But 1 in. increase of radius is 2 in. extension of spring. Therefore if stiffness is S (per spring)

$$2S \times 2 = 93 \cdot 7 \quad \text{or} \quad S = 23 \cdot 4 \text{ lb/in.}$$

G

Centrifugal force on one mass $= \dfrac{1\cdot49}{32\cdot2} \times \dfrac{2\cdot5}{12} \times 89\cdot1^2 = 76\cdot2$ lb,

provided by the extension of two springs. Therefore extension

$$= \frac{76\cdot2}{2 \times 23\cdot4} = \textbf{1\cdot64 lb.}$$

10.5. Inertia Type Governors

Governors of this type are sometimes called shaft governors since they are usually fitted directly to the main engine shaft. The masses then rotate in a vertical plane, and their position is determined mainly by the action of a spring force and centrifugal and tangential forces. The latter force, additional to those of a centrifugal governor, arises from the angular acceleration of the shaft. One such arrangement is shown in Fig. 10.10. These governors can function when the engine speed is being changed, whilst in the centrifugal type the speed has to change significantly before it can be corrected.

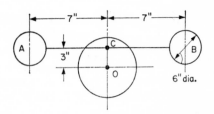

Fig. 10.10. Governor of worked example 10.5

Worked Example (U.L.2. Ext. 1950).

10.5. (a) Shaft governors may be of the centrifugal or of the inertia type. Distinguish between the actions of these two types in controlling the speed of an engine.

(b) A shaft inertia governor consists of an arm AB pivoted at C, C being a fixed point on a disc, concentric with and rigidly attached to the engine shaft. C is offset from the shaft axis O by 3 in. The arm AB is 14 in. long and is symmetrical about C; that is $AC = CB = 7$ in. A weight of 15 lb is attached to each end of the arm at A and B, these weights being in the form of circular discs each 6 in. diameter with their axes parallel to that of the shaft. In the normal position the arm ACB is at right angles to the radius OC. If the speed of the engine increases by 15 rev/min in 2 sec, this increase being at a uniform rate, determine the torque about C needed to hold the arm stationary relative to the concentric disc. Neglect the weight of the arm but carefully explain the reasoning behind any equations you may employ.

SOLUTION

(a) See section 10.5.

(b) Angular acceleration of disc weights $= \dfrac{15}{60} \times 2\pi \times \frac{1}{2}$

$$= 0.785 \text{ rad/sec}^2, \quad \text{i.e. } f = r \cdot a$$

$$= \text{angular acceleration of arm } ACB.$$

The only relative effect on the arm to cause it to rotate relative to the shaft is that due to the angular acceleration since the moments of the centrifugal force, acting along OA and OB, about C cancel out.

Thus the holding couple opposite to the accelerating torque about $C = I \cdot a$ where $I =$ moment of inertia of ACB about C.
$I = 2$ (moment of inertia of the disc A about C)

$$= \frac{2 \times 15}{32.2 \times 12} \left\{ \frac{3^2}{2} + 7^2 \right\} \text{ slug in}^2.$$

Hence   torque $= \dfrac{2 \times 15}{32.2 \times 12} \times 53.5 \times 0.785$

$$= 3.27 \text{ lb in.}$$

Examples

10.6. The weight of each ball of a spring-loaded governor is 6 lb, the maximum and minimum radii of rotation are $4\frac{1}{2}$ in. and $2\frac{1}{2}$ in. and the corresponding values of the control force on each ball are 115 lb and 55 lb. Assuming the control force curve to be a straight line, find the equilibrium speeds for radii of rotation of $2\frac{1}{2}$, $3\frac{1}{2}$ and $4\frac{1}{2}$ in.

If friction of the governor mechanism is equivalent to a force of 1 lb at each ball, what are the extreme equilibrium speeds for a radius of rotation of $3\frac{1}{2}$ in.?   (A.M.I.Mech.E. 1946)

Answer: 359; 378; 387 rev/min, range 375–380 rev/min

10.7. A spring-controlled governor has two rotating masses each weighing 6 lb and the limits of their radius of rotation are 4 and 5 in. Each mass is directly controlled by a spring attached to it and to the casing of the governor, Fig. 10.8. The stiffness of each spring is 40 lb/in. and the force in each spring when the masses are in their mid-position is 80 lb. In addition there is an equivalent constant inward radial force of 15 lb acting on each mass in order to allow for the dead weight of the mechanism. Neglecting friction, find the range of speed of the governor. What would be the required force in each spring when the masses are in their mid-position, for isochronism, and what then would be the speed?   (U.L.1. Ext. 1949)

Answer: 332; 268 rev/min, 165 lb, 484 rev/min.

10.8. A spring-loaded governor of the Hartnell type with vertical axis has arms of equal lengths; when the sleeve is in the mid-position the weight arms are vertical and the operating masses rotate in a circle of 6 in. diameter. The weight of the sleeve is 6 lb and the total sleeve movement is 1 in. If friction is neglected the equilibrium speed with the sleeve in mid-position is 400 rev/min and in this position a drop in speed of $1\frac{1}{2}$ per cent is necessary to overcome a frictional force of 5 lb at the sleeve. The minimum equilibrium speed allowing for friction is to be 368 rev/min. Find the weight of each operating mass, the spring stiffness, the spring compression at mid-position and the maximum equilibrium speed.   (U.L.1. Ext. 1953)

Answer: 6·3 lb, 80 lb/in., 2·03 in., 423 rev/min.

10.9. A Hartnell type spring-loaded governor rotates about a vertical axis. The two rotating masses weigh $2\frac{1}{4}$ lb each, and move at a radius of $4\frac{3}{4}$ in. when the speed is 550 rev/min. At this speed the arms of 4 in. and 3 in. effective length are respectively vertical and horizontal. The equilibrium speed is 575 rev/min when the rotating masses are at their maximum radius of $5\frac{3}{4}$ in.

Determine the stiffness of the spring, the compression of the spring at 550 rev/min and the radius at which the weights rotate when the equilibrium speed is 525 rev/min. (U.L.1. Ext. 1946)

Answer: 108 lb/in., 2·27 in., 4·1 in.

10.10. A spring-controlled governor has two balls each weighing 5 lb. The mean speed is to be 500 rev/min and the variation ±2 per cent. The extreme radii of the path of the balls are 4½ in. and 3½ in. Find the controlling force at the balls in each case. If the effect of friction be ±10 lb at each ball, find the highest and lowest speeds. (U.L.1. Ext. 1960)

Answer: 167 lb, 119 lb, 525, 468 r.p.m.

10.11. In a governor of the Hartnell type the arms of the bell crank levers are equal in length, and those carrying the operating masses are vertical when the governor is rotating at its mean speed of 775 rev/min, with the masses moving in a circle 7 in. diameter. The usual central control spring is replaced by two parallel tension springs directly connecting the operating masses. Find:

(a) the weight of each operating mass if a force of 20 lb is required at the sleeve to maintain it in the mean speed position when the speed is increased from 775 to 800 rev/min;

(b) the stiffness, or rate, of each spring if the ratio of sleeve movement to increase of speed is one inch to 250 rev/min when in the mean position.

(U.L.1. Ext. 1955)

Answer: 2·56 lb, 34·2 lb/in.

10.12. An inertia governor mounted on a flywheel consists of a concentrated mass of 12 lb attached rigidly to an arm which is pivoted at a distance of 7 in. from the centre of the crankshaft. The effective length of the arm, measured from the centre of the mass, is 8 in., and, when the flywheel is rotating at a uniform speed of 90 rev/min, the line joining the pivot to the crankshaft centre makes an angle of 135° with the arm. If the flywheel suddenly starts to change its speed at a rate of 2·5 rad/sec², what will be the torque immediately available for operating the governor system? Discuss the effect for both directions of rotation, also for positive and negative changes of speed. (U.L.2. Ext. 1944 modified)

Answer: 0·158 lb ft.

CHAPTER ELEVEN

BALANCING

11.1. Rotational Balancing

Masses attached to a shaft may not have their centres coinciding with the axis of rotation, and when such a system is rotated the mass centres will move in circular paths. Each eccentric mass will thus exert a centrifugal force on the shaft, and the resultant force, called an unbalanced force, will eventually be carried by the shaft bearings.

The centrifugal force exerted on the shaft by an eccentric mass is given by

$$F = \frac{W}{g} \cdot r \cdot \omega^2 \qquad (11.1)$$

where W is the weight of the mass, r its eccentricity (distance from its centre to the axis of rotation) and ω the angular velocity of the shaft and attached mass.

In an end view of the shaft the centrifugal forces will be acting radially outwards, and in a side view they may act in different vertical planes (for a horizontal shaft) positioned along the shaft. The net effect of the unbalanced force is a tendency to displace the shaft bodily and/or to rotate it, i.e. the effect of a force and/or couple.

The shaft will be in dynamic equilibrium if, therefore,

$$\sum \frac{W}{g} \cdot r \cdot \omega^2 = 0 \quad \text{for the forces, and if}$$

186

$$\frac{W}{g} \cdot r \cdot \omega^2 \cdot d = 0 \quad \text{for the couples,}$$

where d is the distance along the shaft, from some convenient datum, of the plane containing an eccentric mass.

This equilibrium can be investigated by force and couple vector diagrams, and since all masses are rotating with the same angular velocity, diagrams need be drawn only for *one* angular position of the mass system. Also, since for each mass the quantity ω^2/g is common, the force and couple vectors may be drawn to represent

$$\Sigma W \cdot r \quad \text{(force diagram)} \tag{11.2}$$

and $\qquad \Sigma W \cdot r \cdot d \quad \text{(couple diagram).}$

Obviously closure of force and couple vector diagrams will indicate complete *dynamic balance*.

11.2. Static and Dynamic Balance

Apart from unbalance due to centrifugal forces, the eccentricity of the masses may cause the shaft to settle in a particular angular position after it has stopped rotating. This is due to the moment, about the shaft axis, of the weight of the eccentric masses. The turning effect will be a function of the weight and eccentricity of the masses and of the shaft position but it can be shown that for *static balance*, i.e. system stays where it is statically angularly placed, $\Sigma W \cdot r = 0$, and that this is one condition, equation (11.2), for dynamic balance. Thus if a system is in dynamic balance it will also be in static balance. It should be noted that a system in static balance is not necessarily in dynamic balance.

WORKED EXAMPLE (U.L.1. EXT. 1948)

11.1. A, B, C and D are four masses carried by a rotating shaft at radii of 4, 5, 8 and 6 in. respectively. The planes in which the masses revolve are spaced 2 ft apart and the weights of B, C and D are 20, 10 and 8 lb respectively.

Find the required mass A and the relative angular settings of the four masses so that the shaft shall be in complete balance.

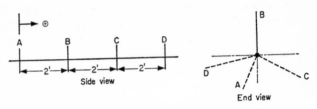

FIG. 11.1. Configuration for worked example 11.1

SOLUTION

Figure 11.1 shows, in side view, the disposition of the planes containing the masses and, in end view, the angular disposition of the masses.

In all rotational balancing problems, vector diagrams are to be drawn, and depending on both the information given and the problem to be solved, so will a decision have to be made whether to draw a diagram for forces ($W . r$) or one for couples ($W . r . d$) first. To facilitate this decision the information is set out in tabular form as in Table 11.1.

TABLE 11.1

Plane	Mass weight W (lb)	Radius r (in.)	$W . r$ force	Distance d(ft) from reference A	$W . r . d$ Couple
A	W_A	4	$4 \times W_A$	0	0
B	20	5	100	+2	200
C	10	8	80	+4	320
D	8	6	48	+6	288

The first four columns of Table 11.1 may be completed from the data given. Note that in the column $W \cdot r$ no units are given since the number quoted is only representative of the *force*; similarly for the column $W \cdot r \cdot d$.

The column for $W \cdot r$ contains three known values and one unknown value, but a vector diagram cannot be uniquely drawn since the angular directions are not known; thus in this example a $W \cdot r \cdot d$ diagram has to be drawn first and a datum for d so selected that the diagram can be drawn. If a datum for d is selected at the plane containing mass A, then the $W \cdot r \cdot d$ value for $A = 0$, since $d = 0$, and so, as shown in Table 11.1, there remain values of $W \cdot r \cdot d$ for masses B, C and D. The position of the shaft where mass B is vertical, as shown in the end view of Fig. 11.1, is considered and a couple $(W \cdot r \cdot d)$ diagram, Fig. 11.2, is drawn to scale.

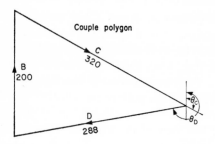

Fig. 11.2. Couple polygon for worked example 11.1

The directions of the vectors of Fig. 11.2 thus give the relative angular positions for the masses; thus $\theta_C = 117\frac{1}{2}°$ and $\theta_D = 259°$.

Now that the angular positions of the masses B, C and D are known, the force diagram $W \cdot r$, shown in Fig. 11.3, is drawn with the closing vector being the value $W_A \cdot r_A$ to give balance. Thus

$$W_A \times 4 = 60 \quad \text{giving} \quad W_A = \textbf{15 lb} \quad \text{and} \quad \theta_A = \textbf{203°}.$$

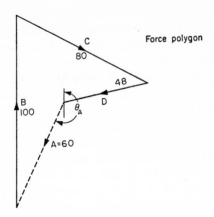

Fig. 11.3. Force polygon for worked example 11.1

WORKED EXAMPLE (U.L.1. EXT. 1952)

11.2. Three pulleys *A*, *B* and *C* are mounted on a shaft, the axial distance from *A* to *B* being 4 ft and from *B* to *C* 3 ft. The pulleys weigh 30 lb, 40 lb and 32 lb respectively and their centres of gravity are 1 in., $\frac{1}{2}$ in., and $\frac{3}{4}$ in. from the centre of rotation of the shaft. The shaft is supported in bearings $5\frac{1}{2}$ ft apart, and the angular positions of the pulleys are adjusted until there is static balance.

Sketch the end view of the shaft, showing the angles between

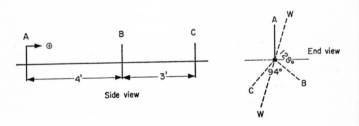

Fig. 11.4. Configuration for worked example 11.2

the lines joining the centre of the shaft and the centres of gravity of the pulleys. What is the force on each bearing, due to lack of balance, when running at 140 rev/min?

It is desired to obtain complete balance by fixing weights to pulleys A and C at 15 in. radius. How much should these weights be? Show their angular position on your sketch.

SOLUTION

The end and side views of the shaft and masses are shown in Fig. 11.4 and data tabulated in Table 11.2.

TABLE 11.2

Plane	Weight (lb)	Radius (in.)	$W \cdot r$	d (A ref.) (ft)	$W \cdot r \cdot d$
A	30	1	30	0	0
B	40	$\frac{1}{2}$	20	+4	80
C	32	$\frac{3}{4}$	24	+7	168

For static balance, the force diagram ($W \cdot r$) must close and this is drawn for the position of $\theta_A = 0$, as shown in Fig. 11.5. The angular positions of the masses in planes B and C, relative to A, are then from the directions of the vectors, $\theta_B = 128°$, $\theta_C = 222°$. The couple diagram ($W \cdot r \cdot d$), plane A as datum for d, is now drawn as shown in Fig. 11·6.

From the couple polygon, the unbalanced couple is that represented by a value 180 and its value in lb ft

$$= 180 \times \frac{\omega^2}{g} \times \frac{1}{12} \text{ lb ft (factor 1/12 because } r \text{ is in inches)}$$

$$= \frac{180}{32 \cdot 2} \times \frac{1}{12} \left(\frac{140}{60} \times 2\pi\right)^2 = 100 \text{ lb ft.}$$

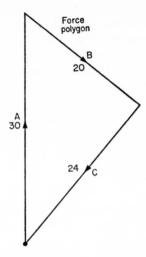

FIG. 11.5. Force polygon for worked example 11.2

This torque, or couple, has to be resisted by the bearings and if force at each bearing is P lb, then

$$P \times \text{distance between bearings} = \text{couple},$$

$$P = \frac{100}{5 \cdot 5} = \textbf{18·2 lb.}$$

Note that the bearings, provided they are $5\frac{1}{2}$ ft apart, may be placed anywhere along the shaft.

If weights in planes A and C are to balance out the couple represented by 180, then these weights must be equal and their angular positions such that one is in the direction of the resultant vector of Fig. 11.6 and one opposite to this. A balancing couple is then obtained without disturbing the balance of the $W \cdot r$ diagram. If W is the required weight, then for C, if A is datum,

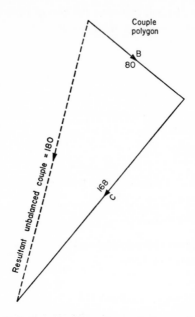

Couple
polygon

B
80

Resultant unbalanced couple = 180

168
C

FIG. 11.6. Couple polygon for worked example **11.2**

$$W \times \frac{15}{12} \times 7 = 180, \qquad \text{giving } W = 1\tfrac{5}{7} \text{ lb, one at an angle of}$$

$16°$ and the other at an angle of $196°$ to A.

WORKED EXAMPLE (U.L.1 EXT. 1947)

11.3. A rotating shaft carries four masses A, B, C and D rigidly attached to it; the mass centres are at $1\tfrac{1}{4}$ in., $1\tfrac{1}{2}$ in., $1\tfrac{5}{8}$ in., $1\tfrac{3}{8}$ in. respectively from the axis of rotation. A, C and D weigh 15 lb, 10 lb and 8 lb; the axial distance between A and B is 16 in. and that between B and C is 20 in.; the eccentricities of A and C are at $90°$ to one another.

Find, for complete balance, (a) the angles between A, B and

D; (b) the axial distance between the planes of revolution of C and D; and (c) the weight of the mass B.

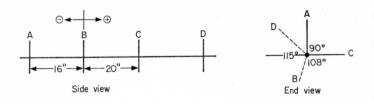

FIG. 11.7. Configuration for worked example 11.3

SOLUTION

Figure 11.7 shows the side and end views, and the data of the example is tabulated in Table 11.3.

TABLE 11.3

Plane	Weight (lb)	Radius (in.)	$W \cdot r$	d (B datum) (in.)	$W \cdot r \cdot d$
A	15	$1\frac{1}{4}$	18·75	-16	-300
B	W_B	$1\frac{1}{2}$	$1·5\,W_B$	0	0
C	10	$1\frac{5}{8}$	16·25	$+20$	$+325$
D	8	$1\frac{3}{8}$	11	d_D	$11d_D$

Since neither W_B nor θ_B and θ_D are known, a $W \cdot r$ diagram cannot be drawn and so in order for a couple ($W \cdot r \cdot d$) diagram to be drawn, B is taken as datum for d and the couple polygon drawn as shown in Fig. 11.8, for the shaft position shown in Fig. 11.7. Note that the datum for d is plane B and that distances to the right are taken as positive, and that to plane A the distance is negative. The $W \cdot r \cdot d$ value, *when negative*, has the vector

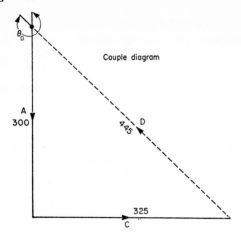

FIG. 11.8. Couple polygon for worked example 11.3

drawn in the *opposite direction* to its positive direction (i.e. $W_A r_A d_A$ downwards).

From the couple polygon, $W_D r_D d_D = 445$, giving $d_D = \dfrac{445}{11}$ = 40·5 in. from B or, distance $CD = $ **20·5 in.**

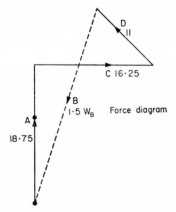

FIG. 11.9. Force polygon for worked example 11.3

The angular position of D is $\theta_D = 313°$.

The force diagram ($W \cdot r$) is now drawn as shown in Fig. 11.9.

From Fig. 11.9, $W_B r_B = 27·5$, giving $W_B = \dfrac{27·5}{1·5} = 18·3$ lb. and

$\theta_B = 198°$ giving angles between A, B and D as shown in Fig. 11.7.

11.3. Out of Balance Forces and Couples Due to Reciprocating Engine Parts

Figure 11.10 shows a diagram of the moving parts of a reciprocating engine cylinder. The force mainly causing rotation of the

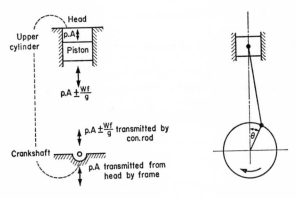

FIG. 11.10. Unbalanced force due to reciprocation

crank is that due to the intensity of gas thrust acting on the piston and can be represented by $p \cdot A$, where p is the pressure and A the effective piston area. This thrust will act not only on the piston face but also on the cylinder head, and under these static forces the complete engine would be in equilibrium. However, due to the motion of the piston, the gas thrust on it may be opposed,

or aided, by an inertia force arising mainly from the linear acceleration of the piston parts. Thus if friction is ignored, the resultant
thrust of the piston on the connecting rod will be,

$$p \cdot A \pm \frac{W}{g} \cdot f \qquad (11.3)$$

where W = weight of the reciprocating parts and f their acceleration.

If the inertia effect of the connecting rod is ignored, or in part
allowed for by a modified value of W, then the force acting on the
crankshaft bearings will be that transmitted by the mechanism
and is equal to

$$p \cdot A \pm \frac{W}{g} \cdot f.$$

The gas thrust acting on the cylinder head is transmitted to the
crankshaft bearings by the engine frame and so there is a resultant,
or unbalanced, force of $p \cdot A \pm (W/g) \cdot f - p \cdot A = (W/g) \cdot f$
acting at the crankshaft in the direction of reciprocation, as
shown in Fig. 11.10. The acceleration f is given approximately by

$$f = \omega^2 \cdot r \left(\cos \theta + \frac{\cos 2\theta}{n} \right), \qquad (11.4)$$

where ω is the angular velocity of the crank in rad/sec, r is the
crank radius in ft, n is the ratio of the length of the connecting
rod l to the length of the crank, i.e. $n = (l/r)$, θ is the angle of the
crank from the dead centre position shown in Fig. 11.10.

Thus the unbalanced force in the line of reciprocation is

$$F = \frac{W}{g} \cdot f = \frac{W}{g} \cdot r \cdot \omega^2 \cos \theta + \frac{W}{g} \cdot \frac{r \cdot \omega^2}{n} \cos 2\theta, \quad (11.5)$$

i.e. $$F = F_1 \cos \theta + F_2 \cos 2\theta. \qquad (11.6)$$

The components $F_1 \cos \theta$ and $F_2 \cos 2\theta$ are called *primary* and *secondary* unbalanced forces respectively.

In the case of a multicylinder in-line engine, primary and secondary forces can arise for each cylinder and so forces will be balanced when

$$\Sigma F_1 \cos \theta = 0 \qquad \text{and} \qquad \Sigma F_2 \cos 2\theta = 0.$$

In addition, the forces, since they do not lie in the same lines of reciprocation, can give rise to couples tending to rotate the engine bodily in the plane of reciprocation. The additional requirements for balance are now

$$\Sigma F_1 \cos \theta \, . \, d = 0 \qquad \text{and} \qquad \Sigma F_2 \cos 2\theta \, . \, d = 0.$$

where d is the distance of the line of reciprocation of a cylinder from some datum which is usually the engine centre.

Investigation of engine balance can be carried out most easily by means of force and couple vector diagrams.

11.4. Vector Representation of Reciprocating Forces and Couples

(a) Primary Vectors

A vector oa whose length represents $(W/g) \, . \, r \, . \, \omega^2$ is drawn, as shown in Fig. 11.11, in the direction of the crank, i.e. at θ to the direction of piston reciprocation. The primary force is then given by ob, the projection of the vector oa on to the direction of reciprocation, and the maximum value of the primary force is the full length of the vector oa. In the case of an engine with several cylinders, a force diagram can be drawn whose sides represent, to scale if necessary, the values $(W/g) \, . \, r \, . \, \omega^2$ for each cylinder drawn in each case in the direction of the respective crank. The addition of vectors gives the maximum unbalanced primary force and this value projected on to the direction of reciprocation gives the unbalance for the engine crank position considered. A closed diagram, of course, indicates force balance.

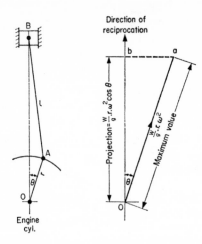

Fig. 11.11. Primary unbalanced vector

Primary couples may be similarly represented. For couples of cylinders on the *positive* side of the reference position, vectors to represent $(W/g) . r . \omega^2 . d$, are drawn in the direction of the respective crank, whilst *negative couples*, i.e. those for cylinders on the negative side of the datum, are drawn in directions *opposite* to the crank position.

(b) Secondary Vectors

The procedure is similar to that for primary vectors except that since the secondary force $= (W/g) . (r . \omega^2/n) . \cos 2\theta$ the vector is drawn, as shown in Fig. 11.12, to represent $(W/g) . (r . \omega^2/n)$ to scale, at an angle of 2θ to the direction of reciprocation.

Secondary couple vectors are drawn to represent, to scale, $(W/g) . (r . \omega^2/n) . d$ either in, or opposite to, the direction of 2θ to the direction of reciprocation.

These vectorial methods are used to solve the following variety of problems.

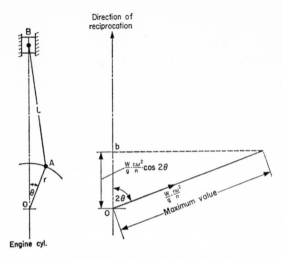

Fig. 11.12. Secondary unbalanced vector

WORKED EXAMPLE (U.L.2. EXT. 1938)

11.4. In a reciprocating engine which has four cylinders in line, the weights of the reciprocating masses are $2\frac{1}{4}$ lb per cylinder. The stroke is 5 in., the length of the connecting rod is 9 in., the cylinders are spaced 5 in. apart. If the cylinders are numbered 1 to 4 from one end, then in an end view the cranks appear at successive intervals of 90° in the order 1, 4, 2, 3. The engine speed is 2000 rev/min. Find, with reference to the central plane of the engine, the maximum value of any primary and secondary out of balance effects.

SOLUTION

The engine is considered in the position shown in Fig. 11.13, i.e. when the crank of cylinder 1 is at dead centre. The angular positions of the cranks are also shown—primary at θ, secondary at 2θ.

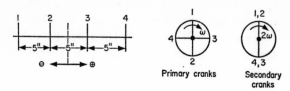

FIG. 11.13. Configuration of engine of worked example 11.4

Primary and secondary forces. Since the cylinder parts are identical, each primary force vector representing $(W/g) . r . \omega^2$ has the same value, and similarly for each secondary force. The primary and secondary force vector diagrams, shown in Fig. 11.14, are then drawn.

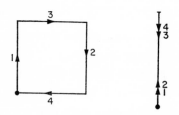

FIG. 11.14. Primary and secondary force diagrams of worked example 11.4

It should be noted that since each vector has the same length and the cranks are equally spaced round 360°, these diagrams must be regular polygons and the engine is balanced for primary and secondary forces. There is also no need to draw diagrams *at all* and in the remaining worked examples when it can be deduced, by observation, that force diagrams are regular polygons they will not be drawn.

Primary couples. Values of the couples are (with datum shown

in Fig. 11.13), $1 = F_1 \cos \theta_1 \, (-7 \cdot 5)$ lb in.; $2 = F_2 \cos \theta_2 \, (-2 \cdot 5)$
lb in.; $3 = F_3 \cos \theta_3 \, (+2 \cdot 5)$ lb in.; $4 = F_4 \cos \theta_4 \, (+7 \cdot 5)$ lb in., and
$F_1 = F_2 = F_3 = F_4 = (W/g) \, . \, r \, . \, \omega^2$. The primary couple diagram
is then drawn to a suitable scale, e.g. 1 in. $\equiv (W/g) \, . \, r \, . \, \omega^2 \times$
5 lb in., as shown in Fig. 11.15.

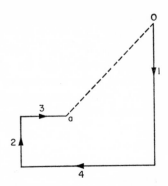

FIG. 11.15. Primary couple diagram for worked example 11.4

The maximum unbalanced primary couple is given by *oa* which,
by measurement, gives

$$7 \cdot 07 \frac{W}{g} \, . \, r \, . \, \omega^2 = 7 \cdot 07 \times \frac{2 \cdot 25}{32 \cdot 2} \times \frac{2 \cdot 5}{12} \left(\frac{2000}{60} \times 2\pi \right)^2 = \textbf{4500 lb in.}$$

Secondary couples. Values are the same as for primary couples
except that $F_1 = F_2 = F_3 = F_4 = (W/g) \, . \, (r \, . \, \omega^2/n)$, and angles
θ_1, θ_2 are doubled. The couple diagram is drawn, as shown in
Fig. 11.16, to a scale of 1 in. $\equiv (W/g) \, . \, (r \, . \, \omega^2/n) \times 5$ lb in.

The maximum unbalanced secondary couple is the sum of the
vectors

$$= 20 \times \frac{W}{g} \, . \, \frac{r \, . \, \omega^2}{n} = 20 \times \frac{2 \cdot 25}{32 \cdot 2} \times \frac{2 \cdot 5}{12} \times \frac{2 \cdot 5}{9} \left(\frac{2000}{60} \times 2\pi \right)^2$$

$$= \textbf{3540 lb in.}$$

FIG. 11.16. Secondary couple diagram for worked example 11.4

WORKED EXAMPLE (A.M.I.Mech.E. 1958)

11.5. A six cylinder in-line engine, of the four-stroke internal combustion type, has a firing order 1, 4, 2, 6, 3, 5. The distance between successive cylinder bores is 4 in., the stroke of each piston is 3 in., the connecting rod length is 6 in., the reciprocating mass per cylinder is 12 oz and the engine speed is 2400 rev/min. (a) Determine, by calculation, the maximum value of the inertia force along each cylinder centre line.
(b) Examine, graphically, the state of balance of the engine so far as primary and secondary forces and couples are concerned, taking a point mid-way between cylinders 3 and 4 as the reference plane.

SOLUTION

(a) It is assumed that the approximate value of $f = \omega^2 \cdot r \left[\cos \theta + (\cos 2\theta/n)\right]$ can be used so that the inertia force in a cylinder is given by $F = (W/g) \cdot \omega^2 [\cos \theta + (\cos 2\theta/n)]$ and the maximum value is when $\theta = 0°$.

$$F_{\max} = \frac{W}{g} \cdot r \cdot \omega^2 \left(1 + \frac{1}{n}\right)$$

$$= \frac{12}{16 \times 32 \cdot 2} \times \frac{1 \cdot 5}{12} \left(\frac{2400}{60} \times 2\pi\right)^2 (1 + \tfrac{1}{4}) \text{ lb.}$$

$$= \mathbf{230 \ lb.}$$

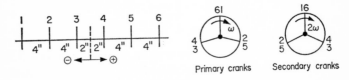

Primary cranks   Secondary cranks

FIG. 11.17. Configuration of the engine of worked example 11.5

(b) Since the engine is working on the four-stroke cycle, the six cylinders have to be fired (piston to come to dead centre) whilst the crank turns through *two revolutions* (one revolution for the two-stroke cycle). The angle between successive cranks is therefore 120° and the "primary" and "secondary" crank positions are as shown in Fig. 11.17.

Primary and secondary forces. Since the reciprocating parts per cylinder are identical and their crank positions (primary and secondary) are equispaced angularly, the primary and secondary force diagrams form regular polygons and indicate balance of both forces.

Primary couples. $1 = F_1 \cos \theta_1 (-10)$; $2 = F_2 \cos \theta_2 (-6)$; $3 = F_3 \cos \theta_3 (-2)$; $4 = F_4 \cos \theta_4 (+2)$; $5 = F_5 \cos \theta_5 (+6)$; $6 = F_6 \cos \theta_6 (+10)$, all lb in., all F values equal to $(W/g) \cdot r \cdot \omega^2$ lb.

The couple diagram is drawn as shown in Fig. 11.18, and closure indicates balance of primary couples.

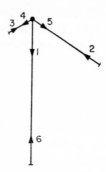

FIG. 11.18. Primary couple diagram for worked example 11.5

Secondary couples. $1 = (F_1/n) \cos \theta_1 (-10)$ lb in. and similarly for others. The couple diagram is drawn as shown in Fig. 11.19, and closure indicates balance of secondary couples. The engine is thus completely balanced for primary and secondary effects.

WORKED EXAMPLE (U.L.2. EXT. 1946)

11.6. An engine having five cylinders in line has successive cranks 144° apart, the distance between cylinder centre lines being 15 in. The reciprocating mass for each cylinder is 35 lb, the crank

FIG. 11.19. Secondary couple diagram for worked example 11.5

radius is 4·5 in. and the connecting rod length is 18 in. The
engine runs at 600 rev/min. Examine the engine for balance of
primary and secondary forces and couples. Determine the maximum values of these and the position of the central crank at which
these maxima occur.

SOLUTION

Since the reciprocating parts per cylinder are identical and the
primary and secondary cranks, as shown in Fig. 11.20, are
equispaced round 360°, then the primary and secondary force
diagrams are regular pentagons indicating that the primary
and secondary forces are in balance.

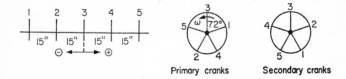

FIG. 11.20. Configuration of the engine of worked example 11.6

Primary couples. (Cylinder 3 as datum.) $1 = F_1 \cos \theta_1 \,(-30)$;
$2 = F_2 \cos \theta_2 \,(-15)$; $3 = 0$; $4 = F_4 \cos \theta_4 \,(+15)$; $5 = F_5 \cos \theta_5$
$(+30)$, all lb in. and all values of $F = (W/g) \cdot r \cdot \omega^2$ lb.

The primary couple diagram is shown in Fig. 11.21, and by

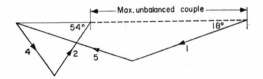

FIG. 11.21. Primary couple diagram for worked example 11.6

measurement the unbalanced couple (maximum)

$$= 2 \cdot 65 \times 15 \times \frac{W}{g} \cdot r \cdot \omega^2$$

$$= 2 \cdot 65 \times 15 \times \frac{35}{32 \cdot 2} \times \frac{4 \cdot 5}{12} \left(\frac{600}{60} \times 2\pi \right)^2 = \textbf{63,800 lb in.}$$

For the engine position shown, the unbalanced couple is 0 since the closing vector is perpendicular to the direction of reciprocation (projection is zero), and this vector will be maximum when it lies wholly in the direction of reciprocation, i.e. when the crank has turned through 90° or 270° from the dead centre position shown.

Secondary couples. (Cylinder 3 as datum.) The secondary couple diagram is as shown in Fig. 11.22, drawn to a scale of 1 in. $\equiv$ $(W/g) \cdot (r\omega^2/n) \times 15$ lb in.

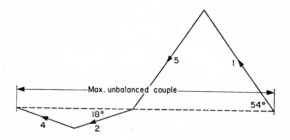

FIG. 11.22. Secondary couple diagram for worked example 11.6

The maximum unbalanced secondary couple is by measurement,

$$4 \cdot 25 \times 15 \times \frac{35}{32 \cdot 2} \times \frac{4 \cdot 5}{12} \times \frac{1}{4} \left(\frac{600}{60} \times 2\pi \right)^2 = \textbf{25,700 lb in.}$$

The maximum occurs when the closing vector is vertical, but since

the secondary cranks are drawn at *twice* crank angles, the engine
has to turn 45° from its position for the vector to turn 90°, and
maximum value is at 45°, 135°, 225°, 315° to dead centre.

11.5. Balance of Twin Cylinder Vee Engine

In the case of radial engines, the consideration of reciprocating
balance is more complex than in in-line engines since there is no
common direction of reciprocation. The simplest method is that
of direct and reverse cranks and one which enables the reader to
visualise the unbalanced effects. However, this is given in detail
in Volume II. For the simple case of a two cylinder vee engine a
mathematical treatment is tolerable for primary forces only.

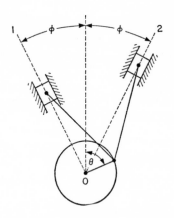

FIG. 11.23. Twin cylinder vee engine

Figure 11.23 shows a vee engine with its cylinders equispaced at
an angle of ϕ on either side of the vertical. The cylinders work off
a common crank whose position is θ after the vertical position, so
that the crank angle for cylinder 1 is $(\theta + \phi)$ and for cylinder 2
is $(\theta - \phi)$.

The primary force for cylinder 1 is thus $F_1 = (W/g) \cdot r \cdot \omega^2 \cos (\theta + \phi)$, acting in direction 1 to 0, whilst that for cylinder 2 is $F_2 = (W/g) \cdot r \cdot \omega^2 \cos (\theta - \phi)$, acting in direction 2 to 0. The total vertical component for these $= V = F_1 \cos \phi + F_2 \cos \phi =$

$$\frac{W}{g} \cdot r \cdot \omega^2 \cos (\theta + \phi) \cdot \cos \phi + \frac{W}{g} \cdot r \cdot \omega^2 \cos (\theta - \phi) \cdot \cos \phi. \quad (11.7)$$

The total horizontal component for these $H = F_1 \sin \phi - F_2 \sin \phi$ (to the right if positive)

$$= \frac{W}{g} \cdot r \cdot \omega^2 \cos (\theta + \phi) \cdot \sin \phi - \frac{W}{g} \cdot r \cdot \omega^2 \cos (\theta - \phi) \cdot \sin \phi. \quad (11.8)$$

The resultant effective primary force on the engine is thus $F = \sqrt{(V^2 + H^2)}$ acting at an angle $\tan \beta = V/H$. Eqns. (11.7) and (11.8) may be written in the form,

$$V = \frac{W}{g} \cdot r \cdot \omega^2 \cos \phi \, [\cos (\theta + \phi) + \cos (\theta - \phi)]$$

$$= \frac{W}{g} \cdot r \cdot \omega^2 \cos \theta \, (1 + \cos 2\phi), \quad (11.9)$$

and similarly,

$$H = \frac{W}{g} \cdot r \cdot \omega^2 \sin \theta \, (1 - \cos 2\phi). \quad (11.10)$$

There is little to be gained by developing equations (11.9) and (11.10) any further, but by observation of these equations, when $\phi = 90°$, i.e. with a 180° vee engine, there is no vertical component, primary unbalanced force acting on the engine.

Examples

11.7. A rough casting for a rotor weighing 450 lb is mounted on centres 46 in. apart ready for machining. It is given static balance by two masses A and B in planes which are situated 20 in. and 16 in. respectively on either side of the plane containing the mass centre. The weights of the masses A and B are 20 lb and 24 lb respectively, and their mass centres are at 90° to each other relative to the axis of the casting and of 15 in. and 18 in. radius respectively. Determine the eccentricity of the mass centre of the casting, its angular position relative to that of mass A, and the forces on the centres when the rotor with attached masses A and B is run at 50 rev/min.

Answer: 1·17 in., 235°, 14·1 lb.   (U.L.1. Ext. 1949)

11.8. Four pulleys A, B, C, D are mounted on a shaft. Due to carelessness in manufacture, the centres of gravity of the pulleys do not lie on the shaft axis, but are displaced slightly from it as indicated by the following table:

Pulley weight in lb	Displacement of c.g. from axis
A 1000	0·3 in.
B 1500	0·24 in. at 30° to A
C 1500	0·24 in. at 90° to A
D 1000	0·18 in. at 150° to A

This shaft is carried in bearings at E and F, the pulleys and bearings being situated so that the axial distances along the shaft are $AB = 24$ in., $AC = 36$ in., $AD = 60$ in., $AE = 12$ in., $AF = 48$ in. If this system rotates at 300 rev/min. determine the magnitude of the bearing reactions arising from the lack of balance, and the directions of these reactions relative to the out of balance force from pulley A.

Answer: 1200 lb at 295°; 1780 lb at 198°.   (U.L.1. Ext. 1950)

11.9. A shaft turning at a uniform speed carries two uniform discs A and and B of masses 10 lb and 8 lb respectively. The mass centres of the discs are each 0·1 in. from the axis of rotation. The radii to the mass centres are at right angles. The shaft is carried in bearings C and D between A and B such that $AC = 1$ ft, $AD = 3$ ft, $AB = 4$ ft. It is required to make the dynamic loading on the bearing equal and a minimum for any given shaft speed by adding a mass at a radius of 1 in. in a plane E.

Determine:

(a) the magnitude of the mass in plane E and its angular position relative to the radial through the mass centre in plane A;

(b) the distance of plane E from plane A;

(c) the dynamic loading on each bearing when the mass in plane E has been attached and the shaft turns at 200 rev/min. (U.L.1. Ext. 1954)

Answer: Solution 1 resultant couple = 0, resultant force midway between CD (a) 2·8 lb, 141°, (b) 1·085 ft, (c) 0·714 lb. Solution 2 resultant forces at bearings zero (a) 1·28 lb, 219°, (b) 1·56 ft, (c) 12·8 lb.

11.10. The four cylinders A, B, C and D of a vertical engine are spaced at 24 in., 18 in. and 24 in. centres. The reciprocating masses of cylinders A and D each weigh 160 lb and their cranks are at 90° to one another. The stroke is 12 in. and the connecting rod length is 20 in. Determine the weights of the reciprocating masses for B and C and their crank positions relative to that of A if all primary forces and couples balance one another.

Calculate the maximum unbalanced secondary force when the engine is running at 450 rev/min.

Answer: 430 lb, 150°, 300°, 7750 lb. (U.L.1. Ext. 1948)

11.11. A four cylinder in-line two-stroke oil engine has the cranks equally spaced along the shaft and so arranged as to give uniform firing intervals. If the cranks are numbered 1 to 4 from one end, show in an end view the relative positions of the four cranks which will give (a) the least unbalanced primary effect, and (b) the least unbalanced secondary effect.

Answer: Several firing orders will do. (A.M.I.Mech.E. 1948)

11.12. A four-stroke engine has five identical cylinders in line, spaced at equal intervals of 4 in. The reciprocating parts per cylinder weigh 1·5 lb, the piston stroke is 3 in. and the connecting rods are 6 in. long between centres. The firing order is 1, 4, 5, 3, 2 and the engine speed is 2400 rev/min. Show that the engine is in balance for primary and secondary forces. Determine the maximum value of the primary and secondary couple acting on the engine and state the positions of No. 1 crank at which these maximum values occur. Take the plane of No. 3 cylinder as the reference plane for couple calculations.

(A.M.I.Mech.E. 1959)

Answer: 2350 lb in., 29°, 209°; 1760 lb in., 20°, 110°, 200°, 290°.

11.13. The firing order in a six cylinder four-stroke in line engine is 1, 4, 2, 6, 3, 5. The piston stroke is 4 in. and the length of each connecting rod is 8 in. The pitch distances between cylinder centre lines are 4 in., 4 in., 6 in., 4 in., 4 in. The reciprocating mass per cylinder = 1·5 lb and the engine runs at 3000 rev/min. Determine the out of balance primary and secondary forces and couples taking a plane midway between cylinders 3 and 4 as reference. (A graphical solution is suggested. Label all diagrams and vectors.)

Answer: Engine balanced.   (U.L.2. Ext. 1953)

11.14. Two alternate designs are contemplated for a single acting two-stroke diesel engine having six cylinders in-line with centre lines spaced 36 in. apart. In the end view the cranks are to be 60° apart either in order 1, 5, 3, 6, 2, 4 or in order 1, 4, 5, 2, 3, 6. The stroke is to be 10 in. and each connecting rod 22 in. long. The reciprocating parts of each cylinder weigh 2100 lb and the rotating parts 1500 lb at crank radius. The engine rotates at 250 rev/min. Show that with either arrangement the primary and secondary forces are balanced and that secondary moments are balanced in the first case and the primary moments in the second. Calculate the maximum unbalanced moment in each case.

Answer: 330,000 lb ft; 87,500 lb ft.   (U.L.2. Ext. 1952)

CHAPTER TWELVE

GYROSCOPIC ACTION

GYROSCOPIC action takes place when the axis about which a body is spinning is moved in a particular angular way, such angular motion of the axis being called precession. Thus, for example, gyroscopic action can occur in an automobile when the axes, about which the engine or transmission rotate, are precessed by the automobile moving round a curve.

12.1. Angular Momentum and Velocity Vectors

The vector representation of linear quantities such as velocity is simple since a straight line drawn in a particular direction and of definite length is all that is needed. With angular quantities, however, representation is a little more involved owing to the necessity of drawing, on a plain sheet of paper, something that has motion about, as opposed to along, an axis or direction

Vector representation is made by using the analogy with the motion of a right-handed screw. If such a screw is rotated its motion along the axis of rotation will be proportional to its angular motion about the axis. Thus a vector drawn to represent the axial velocity will also represent, as shown in Fig. 12.1, the angular velocity.

Since angular momentum h is given by the product of moment of inertia I and angular velocity ω, then $h = I . \omega$ and the vector representing ω will, to a different scale, also represent the angular momentum of the body about the axis of spin.

H

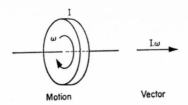

FIG. 12.1 Angular momentum vector

12.2. Gyroscopic Action of a Rotating Disc Using Momentum Vectors

A disc is shown in Fig. 12.2, spinning about an axis OO. If a torque is applied, as shown, to act about an axis perpendicular to the axis of spin, then the disc does not turn about this axis but does so about a third axis, perpendicular to the other two. This effect is known as the gyroscopic action and the velocity about the third axis is called the velocity of precession ω_p.

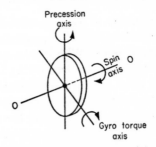

FIG. 12.2. Axes of reference of a spinning disc

The explanation of the gyroscopic action is as follows: a disc of polar moment of inertia I about its horizontal axis of spin is rotating, as shown in the views of Fig. 12.3, at ω rad/sec. It is made to precess in the horizontal plane, (plan view), so that in a small period of time the angle of precession is $\delta\theta$ rad.

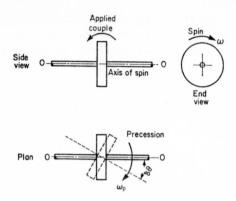

Fig. 12.3. Views of a spinning disc

For simplicity it is assumed that whilst precessing the spin velocity remains constant. The vector representing the initial angular momentum $I \cdot \omega$ is vector oa, shown in Fig. 12.4, and drawn in the horizontal plane of precession.

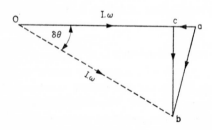

Fig. 12.4. Angular momentum vectors of a spinning disc

Precession causes the axis of spin to swing through angle $\delta\theta$ and the vector for the position after δt sec is vector ob. Whilst the magnitude of momentum $I \cdot \omega$, has not changed, there is, due to change of position, a change of momentum as represented by vector *bc*. This vector is resolved into vector *ac* in direction *ao*, and vector *cb* in a direction which is perpendicular to *ao*. From the trigonometry of Fig. 12.4, the change in angular momentum along $ao = I \cdot \omega - I \cdot \omega \cdot \cos \delta\theta$ which, if $\delta\theta$ is small, reduces to zero.

The change in angular momentum perpendicular to *ao* $= I \cdot \omega \cdot \sin \delta\theta$ which, if $\delta\theta$ is small, reduces to $I \cdot \omega \cdot \delta\theta$. This change occurs in time δt and so the rate of change of angular momentum $= I \cdot \omega \cdot (\delta\theta/\delta t)$, but $(\delta\theta/\delta t)$ is the rate of precession ω_p, thus rate of change of angular momentum $= I \cdot \omega \cdot \omega_p$ and hence, applied torque (gyroscopic torque) $= I \cdot \omega \cdot \omega_p$ (12.1).

The sense and plane of action of the gyroscopic torque must be such as to *give* vector *cb* drawn in plan view. This vector represents a torque to act as shown in Fig. 12.3. This will be the *torque on the gyroscope to make it precess*, the effect of the gyroscope on the shaft holding it will be equal in magnitude but opposite in sense to the gyroscopic torque.

Note that the analysis given above refers to a simple gyroscope i.e. a thin disc, and should not be applied to a gyroscope consisting of a body of substantial thickness and, or, having a non symmetrical section, the implication of which is explained in Volume II.

WORKED EXAMPLE (A.M.I.Mech.E. 1959)

12.1. The crankshaft of a motor-car engine is parallel to the longitudinal axis of the car and rotates in a clockwise direction when viewed from the front. The rotating parts of the engine weigh 400 lb with a mean radius of gyration of 4 in.

Calculate the magnitude of the gyroscopic couple and its effect on the loading of the four wheels when the engine is running at 3000 rev/min and the car turns to the right on a radius of 150 ft at a mean speed of 45 m.p.h.

Show clearly the gyroscopic effects of the engine when an irregularity of the road surface causes the nose of the car to rise suddenly.

SOLUTION

When the car turns to the right as shown in the plan view of Fig. 12.5, all parts of it rotate in a clockwise direction and the engine is precessed. The angular velocity of precession

$$= \frac{\text{linear velocity } (v)}{\text{radius of curve } (r)} = \frac{66}{150} \text{ rad/sec} = \omega_p.$$

The angular velocity of spin of the engine $= (3000/60) \times 2\pi$ rad/sec. The moment of inertia of the engine about its axis of spin (I)

$$= \frac{400}{32 \cdot 2} \left(\frac{4}{12} \right)^2 \text{ slugs ft}^2.$$

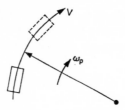

FIG. 12.5. Precession of the car in worked example 12.1

Thus gyroscopic torque due to precession of the engine is

$$T = I \cdot \omega \cdot \omega_p = \frac{400}{32 \cdot 2} \times \left(\frac{4}{12} \right)^2 \times \frac{3000}{60} \times 2\pi \times \frac{66}{150} = \textbf{191 lb ft.}$$

The momentum vectors for the original and new positions are shown in Fig. 12.6. The torque which produces the change vector is in a clockwise direction when looking, as shown in Fig. 12.6, in the sideways view. This torque is the one *applied to the gyro.*, and will arise from the road reacting on the wheels. The effect of the gyroscope on the car and road is opposite to this. Either

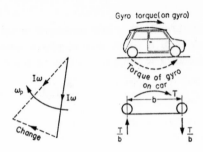

FIG. 12.6. Momentum vectors and torque of car in worked example 12.1

way, the effect is to increase the road forces on the rear wheels by an amount $T/2b$ each, and to decrease those on the front wheel by an amount $T/2b$ each. (T is the gyro. torque and b the wheel base.) Note that no dimension for b is given in this problem and so the values of road reaction changes cannot be numerically evaluated.

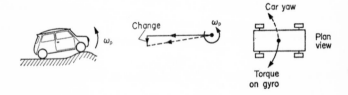

FIG. 12.7. Gyroscopic action for the car of worked example 12.1

When the nose of the car is raised the effect is to cause a precession in a vertical plane, and the engine spin vectors are shown in Fig. 12.7, drawn in the side view. The change of momentum is brought about by a gyro. torque in a clockwise sense in plan view. The reaction to the gyroscopic torque is in an anti-clockwise direction, thus causing the car to yaw to the left.

WORKED EXAMPLE (U.L.2. EXT. 1952)

12.2. The turbine rotor of a ship weighs 30 tons, has a radius of gyration of 2 ft and rotates at 2400 rev/min in a clockwise direction when viewed from aft. The ship pitches through a total angle of 15°, $7\frac{1}{2}$° above and $7\frac{1}{2}$° below the horizontal, the motion being simple harmonic and having a period of 12 sec. Determine the maximum gyroscopic couple on the holding-down bolts on the turbine and the direction of yaw as the bow rises.

SOLUTION

The *gyroscope* is the turbine which spins at a speed of 2400 rev/min and which is precessed as the ship pitches (i.e. bow rises and falls).

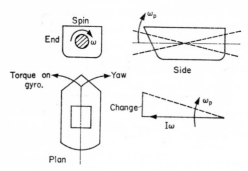

FIG. 12.8. Gyroscopic action for ship of worked example 12.2

Figure 12.8 shows the plan, end and side views of the ship and turbine. The maximum gyroscopic torque will occur when the precessional velocity is a maximum, i.e. when the ship is in mean position of harmonic motion. Reference to Chapter 4, will show that

$$\omega_p \text{ (max)} = \text{constant} \times \text{angular amplitude,}$$

where constant $= 2\pi/\text{periodic time} = \pi/6$.

Hence, gyroscopic torque

$$= I . \omega . \omega_p = \frac{30 \times 2240}{32 \cdot 2} \times 4 \times \frac{\pi}{6} \times \frac{7 \cdot 5}{180} \times \frac{2400}{60} \times 2\pi$$

$$= \textbf{144,000 lb ft.}\ \text{or,}\ \textbf{64·2 ton ft.}$$

Figure 12.8 shows the spin vectors in the side view and from the change vector, the gyroscopic torque will act anticlockwise in plan view, i.e. to port. The gyroscope will therefore cause the ship to swing to the right, i.e. to starboard.

WORKED EXAMPLE (A.M.I.Mech.E. 1953)

12.3. The frame of a gyroscope in Fig. 12.9 is supported at O so that it can turn freely in all directions. The wheel is a uniform

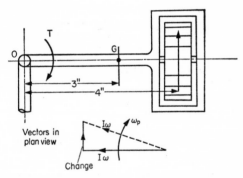

FIG. 12.9. Gyroscopic frame of worked example 12.3

disc of 2·5 in. diameter weighing 1·375 lb with its centre 4 in. from O. The frame alone weighs 0·75 lb with centre of gravity G 3 in. from O. If the wheel spins as shown at 10,000 rev/min with its axle in the horizontal plane, find the time required for the axle to make one revolution about O. Show the direction of this rotation on the diagram. Find also the vertical and horizontal forces exerted by the support on the frame at O.

SOLUTION

The torque on the gyroscope is clockwise in the vertical plane and this gives rise to a change of momentum vector in a horizontal plane. The vector diagram is shown in Fig. 12.9. Torque $T = (\frac{3}{4} \times 3) + (1\frac{3}{4} \times 4) = 7 \cdot 75$ lb in. $= 0 \cdot 646$ lb ft due to the weight of the frame and wheel. Thus,

$$\omega_p = \frac{T}{I \cdot \omega} = 0 \cdot 646 \left/ \left(\frac{1 \cdot 375}{32 \cdot 2} \times \frac{2 \cdot 5^2}{8} \times \frac{1}{144} \times \frac{10,000}{60} \times 2\pi \right) \right.$$

$$= 2 \cdot 66 \text{ rad/sec.}$$

Time to make 1 revolution at this velocity $= t = (2\pi/2 \cdot 66)$ = **2.36 sec.**

Vertical force at O is due to weight $= \frac{3}{4} + 1\frac{3}{8} = \mathbf{2\frac{1}{8}}$ **lb.**

Horizontal force at O is due to centrifugal force of the frame and wheel precessing at $2 \cdot 66$ rad/sec

$$= \frac{\omega_p^2}{g} \, [W_1 \, r_1 + W_2 \, r_2]$$

$$= \frac{2 \cdot 66^2}{32 \cdot 2} \, (0 \cdot 75 \times \tfrac{3}{12} + 1\tfrac{3}{8} \times \tfrac{4}{12}) \text{ lb}$$

$$= \mathbf{0 \cdot 142} \text{ lb.}$$

Examples

12.4. The following particulars are given for a motor vehicle: Total weight, 3300 lb; wheel base, $10\frac{1}{2}$ ft; track width, 5 ft; centre of gravity 6 ft behind the front axle and 3 ft 2 in. above road level; moment of inertia of two front wheels, 250 lb ft^2; moment of inertia of two rear wheels, 350 lb ft^2; moment of inertia of parts turning at engine speed, 50 lb ft^2; wheel diameter, $2\frac{1}{2}$ ft; gear ratio from engine to road wheels, 10 to 1. The engine turns in a clockwise direction when viewed from the front of the vehicle. The vehicle travels at a constant speed of 50 m.p.h. and enters a right hand curve of 500 ft radius. Determine:

(a) The vertical load on each wheel taking into account
    (i) gravitational effects;
    (ii) centrifugal effects;
    (iii) the gyroscopic effects due to the engine rotation.
(b) The rolling couple acting on the vehicle due to the gyroscopic effect of
    the road wheels.   (U.L.2. Ext. 1954)

Answer: (a) (i) each front 707·5 lb, each rear 942·5 lb. (ii) decrease of front inner 298 lb, increase front outer 298 lb, decrease of rear inner 398 lb, increase rear outer 398 lb. (iii) fronts decreased by 6·35 lb each, rears increased by 6·35 lb each. (b) 160 lb ft.

12.5. A rear engined automobile is travelling round a track of 300 ft mean radius. Each of the four wheels has a moment of inertia of 37·5 lb ft² and an effective diameter of 24 in. The rotating parts of the engine have a moment of inertia of 20 lb ft², the engine axis is parallel to the rear axle and the crankshaft rotates in the same sense as the road wheels. The gear ratio, engine to back axle is 3:1. The vehicle weighs 3000 lb and has its centre of gravity 18 in. above the road level. The width of the track of the vehicle is 60 in.

Determine the limiting speed of the vehicle around the curve for all four wheels to maintain contact with the road surface, if this is not cambered.

Answer: 85 m.p.h.   (U.L.2. Ext. 1953)

12.6. Derive from first principles the expression for the gyroscopic torque required to give a precessional velocity Ω to a body having a moment of inertia I and a spinning velocity ω. The turbine of a ship weighs 6 tons and has a radius of gyration 19·5 in. It rotates at 1800 rev/min clockwise when looking forward from the stern. Determine the gyroscopic effects set up:
(a) If the ship, when travelling at 15 knots, steers to the left in a curve of
    200 ft radius.
(b) If the ship is pitching and the bow descending with its maximum
    velocity. The pitching is simple harmonic, the periodic time being
    20 sec, and the total angular movement between extreme positions 10°.
(c) If the ship is rolling and at a certain instant has an angular velocity
    0·02 rad/sec clockwise when looking from the stern. Assume 1 knot =
    1·69 ft/sec.   (U.L.2. Ext. 1950)

Answer: (a) 140 ton in., (b) 30·5 ton in. (c) none since roll and spin axes same and thus no precession.

12.7. A uniform thin disc of radius r ft and weight W lb is given an angular velocity Ω rad/sec about its polar axis, and this axis is precessed with an angular velocity ω rad/sec.

(a) State the magnitude of the gyroscopic torque and show by means of a diagram the sense in which it acts.

(b) Explain how this torque is produced.

A pair of wheels and an axle are rolling along a straight horizontal railway track at 70 m.p.h. An irregularity in one rail results in a wheel descending a vertical distance of 0·01 ft while travelling a horizontal distance of 2 ft. Given that the vertical motion of the wheel is simple harmonic, of amplitude 0·01 ft, determine the maximum gyroscopic torque on the wheels and axle. The effective track width is 5 ft. The effective radius of each wheel is 2½ ft. The combined moment of inertia of the wheels and axle is 4000 lb ft².

Answer: 827 lb ft.

(U.L.2. Ext. 1955)

CHAPTER THIRTEEN

ELASTIC VIBRATIONS

An UNDERSTANDING of the theory of vibrating mechanical systems is important to a designer, and an engineering student will find that two major fields are involved. These are, briefly, the design of machines and automatic control systems. Attention is given in Volumes I and II to the former and this will imply a consideration of the vibration of such elements as springs, shafts, beams, etc., and combinations of these.

13.1. Degrees of Freedom and Elastic Constraints

Although a link of a machine is designed on a basis of its rigidity, when loaded it will deform and if such deformation is elastic the link is capable of vibrating. In addition, links of a machine may be constrained to move with relative motion controlled by elastic members, such as springs, and then the links may be vibrated as complete units relative to each other. Thus a machine may be capable of vibrating in many ways, and to facilitate an ordered examination of these modes of vibration, analysis is carried out in terms of degrees of freedom. A system will have as many degrees of freedom as there are parameters required to specify the motion, each rigid body capable of, but probably not having, three translational and three rotational degrees.

A further classification can be made according to the elastic form of constraint and, in engineering, these commonly act in longitudinal, torsional and flexural manner, as shown in Fig. 13.1.

Finally, the nature of the vibration will depend on the mode of

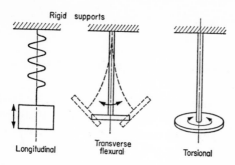

FIG. 13.1. Elastic constraints and types of vibration

excitation which may be natural or forced, and whether damping is present. In natural vibrations, the system is deformed, the deforming influence removed and the system allowed to vibrate freely. With forced vibrations the deforming influence is repetitive in character.

13.2. System Representation and General Method of Analysis

Many systems are so complex that they require consideration in simplified form for a reasonable analysis to be made. This is generally done in the following stages:

(a) Using engineering experience the system is imagined to consist of inelastic masses connected together by massless springs and thus represented by a mass–spring diagram.

(b) The simplified vibrating system is considered to be in some general vibrating position and its dynamic equilibrium, or energy etc., is expressed in the form of an equation of motion.

(c) The equation of motion is solved by reference to standard differential equations or mathematical guessing or, if there are several simultaneous equations, computor assistance may be needed.

(d) The final solution has then to be interpreted in terms of the original system and this will usually again call for engineering experience.

13.3. Natural Vibrations of Single Degree of Freedom Systems

(a) *Longitudinal*

Figure 13.2 shows a mass of weight W hanging freely from a rigid support by means of an elastic member of stiffness S. The weight of the suspended mass causes a static deflection of δ as shown. The mass is disturbed in a vertical direction and then allowed to make natural longitudinal vibrations with a single degree of vertical freedom.

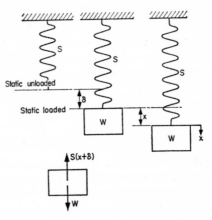

FIG. 13.2. Natural longitudinal vibrations

Consider the mass in a position where it is, as shown in Fig. 13.2, displaced x from the static loaded position.

Forces acting on the mass are its weight W and a force due to the spring extension. The spring force is the spring stiffness times the spring extension $= S(x + \delta)$.

The resultant force on the mass in the downwards (i.e. positive) direction of $x = W - S(x + \delta)$
$$= W - S.x - S.\delta.$$

But in the static position, $W = S \cdot \delta$ and hence, resultant force on mass $= - S \cdot x$ and so by Newton's Law,

$$- S \cdot x = \text{mass} \times \text{acceleration} = \frac{W}{g} \cdot \frac{\mathrm{d}^2 x}{\mathrm{d}t^2}$$

or

$$\frac{W}{g} \cdot \frac{\mathrm{d}^2 x}{\mathrm{d}t^2} + S \cdot x = 0$$

giving,

$$\frac{\mathrm{d}^2 x}{\mathrm{d}t^2} + \frac{S \cdot g}{W} \cdot x = 0. \qquad (13.1)$$

The equation of motion is thus,

$$\frac{\mathrm{d}^2 x}{\mathrm{d}t^2} + b \cdot x = 0, \qquad (13.2)$$

where, $b = S \cdot g / W$.

The solution of equation (13.2) is

$$x = A \cdot \sin \sqrt{b} \cdot t + B \cdot \cos \sqrt{b} \cdot t, \qquad (13.3)$$

which should be recognised as that for simple harmonic motion (see Chapter 4).

Of interest to a designer is the amplitude and frequency of the vibration since both are of significance in fatigue calculations. The amplitude is given by

$$x_0 = \sqrt{(A^2 + B^2)} \qquad (13.4)$$

and the frequency f_N is given by

$$f_N = \frac{1}{t_N} = \frac{\omega_N}{2\pi} = \frac{\sqrt{b}}{2\pi} = \frac{1}{2\pi} \sqrt{\frac{S \cdot g}{W}}, \qquad (13.5)$$

t_N = periodic time of natural vibration, ω_N = circular frequency of natural vibration.

A useful practical form of the frequency equation is

$f_N = \dfrac{1}{2\pi}\sqrt{\dfrac{g}{\delta}}$, and if δ is the static deflection in *inches* and f_N the frequency in vib/min., then

$$f_N = \frac{187\cdot8}{\sqrt{\delta}} \text{ vib/min.} \qquad (13.6)$$

An alternative method of arriving at the equation of motion is to consider the energy of the system. The natural vibration continues owing to the continuous interchange of the kinetic energy of the moving mass and the strain energy stored in the elastic spring. In the absence of any losses of energy, the sum of the kinetic and strain energies (or potential) will remain constant.

Thus $\qquad\qquad \dfrac{W}{2g} \cdot \left(\dfrac{\mathrm{d}x}{\mathrm{d}t}\right)^2 + \tfrac{1}{2}\,S \cdot x^2 = \text{constant}$

which, on differentiation, yields

$$\frac{W}{2g} \times 2 \times \frac{\mathrm{d}x}{\mathrm{d}t} \cdot \frac{\mathrm{d}^2x}{\mathrm{d}t^2} + \tfrac{1}{2}\,.\,S\,.\,2x\,.\,\frac{\mathrm{d}x}{\mathrm{d}t} = 0$$

or $\qquad\qquad\qquad \dfrac{W}{g} \cdot \dfrac{\mathrm{d}^2x}{\mathrm{d}t^2} + S \cdot x = 0$

which is the same equation as before.

Note that the maximum kinetic energy occurs at mid-position when the strain energy (extra to the static quantity) is zero, and that the maximum strain energy is at the extreme displacement when the kinetic energy is zero. Thus if the total energy is constant, the maximum kinetic energy equals the maximum strain energy, although they do not occur at the same time. This principle will be seen later to be of value when dealing with approximate methods for systems with several degrees of freedom.

(b) Transverse

Figure 13.3 shows a beam carrying a single load whose weight is large compared to that of the beam. The motion of the mass, for

FIG. 13.3. Natural transverse vibrations

vibrations of small amplitude, can be considered to be of a single degree of vertical freedom with the elastic constraint provided by the bending of the beam. There is no basic difference between this system and the one previously considered. Thus

$$f_N = \frac{187 \cdot 8}{\sqrt{\delta}} \text{ vib/min,} \qquad (13.7)$$

where δ is the *static* deflection of the beam at the point of attachment of the load and due to the load. Note δ in inches.

(c) *Torsional*

Figure 13.4 shows a shaft mounted horizontally with one end fixed, and carrying a rotor of moment of inertia I at the free end. The system is angularly displaced and allowed to make torsional

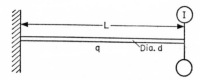

FIG. 13.4. Natural torsional vibrations

vibrations about a horizontal axis. If the torsional stiffness of the shaft is q lb ft/rad, then the equation of motion of the natural torsional single degree of freedom vibrations of the rotor is

$$I \cdot \frac{d^2\theta}{dt^2} + q \cdot \theta = 0. \qquad (13.8)$$

θ is the angular displacement of the rotor relative to a fixed datum. The frequency is given by

$$f_N = \frac{1}{2\pi} \sqrt{\frac{q}{I}}. \tag{13.9}$$

Equation (13.9) can be developed for the case of a *circular section* shaft since

$$q = \frac{T}{\theta} = \frac{G \cdot J}{L}$$

giving

$$f_N = \frac{1}{2\pi} \sqrt{\frac{G \cdot J}{I \cdot L}} \tag{13.10}$$

where G is the modulus of rigidy of the shaft;

J is the polar second moment of area of the shaft section equal to $\pi d^4/32$ if d is the shaft diameter;

I is the moment of inertia of the attached rotor about the axis of vibration, and

L is the length of the shaft.

WORKED EXAMPLE

13.1. A disc flywheel weighing 22 lb and having a diameter of 12 in. is suspended from a rod $2\frac{1}{2}$ ft long and 1 in. diameter as shown in Fig. 13.1. The modulus of rigidity of the rod is 12×10^6 lb/in² and its modulus of elasticity is 30×10^6 lb/in². Determine, ignoring the mass of the rod, the frequencies of natural longitudinal, transverse and torsional single degree of freedom vibrations.

SOLUTION

(a) Longitudinal. The extension of the rod (static) if carrying a load of 22 lb

$$= \delta = \frac{W \cdot L}{a \cdot E} = \frac{22 \times 2\frac{1}{2} \times 12}{(\pi/4) \times 1^2 \times 30 \times 10^6} = 0.000028 \text{ in.}$$

$$f_N = \frac{187.8}{\sqrt{0.000028}} = \frac{187.8}{0.00528} = \textbf{35,600 vib/min.}$$

(b) Transverse. For a cantilever carrying a concentrated load at the free end, the static deflection at the load is

$$\delta = \frac{W \cdot L^3}{3EI} = \frac{22 \times 30^3 \times 64}{3 \times 30 \times 10^6 \times \pi \times 1^4} = 0.134 \text{ in.}$$

$$f_N = \frac{187.8}{\sqrt{0.134}} = \textbf{513 vib/min.}$$

(c) Torsional. Torsional stiffness $= q = G \cdot J/L$ which in feet units gives $q = \dfrac{12 \times 10^6 \times 144 \times \pi \times 1^4}{32 \times 12^4 \times 2\frac{1}{2}} = 0.327 \times 10^4$ lb ft/rad.

$$f_N = \frac{1}{2\pi} \sqrt{\frac{q}{I}} = \frac{1}{2\pi} \sqrt{\frac{3270}{(22/32\cdot2) \times (12^2/8) \times (1/144)}} \text{ vib/sec}$$

$$= \textbf{1865 vib/min.}$$

WORKED EXAMPLE

13.2. A uniform rigid bar, length 10 ft, weighs 70 lb and is hinged at one end so that it is free to vibrate in a vertical plane. When at rest it is maintained in a horizontal position by a light vertical spring, situated 3 ft from the hinge. The stiffness of the spring is 10 lb/in. Determine the frequency of natural vibrations of small amplitude.

The system is now turned so that the bar hangs at an angle of 45° to the vertical with the spring acting in a direction perpendicular to the bar. Determine the frequency of small vibrations in the new position.

SOLUTION

Let the bar be in the position of θ below the mean as shown in Fig. 13.5.

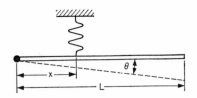

FIG. 13.5. Vibrating system of worked example 13.2

The change of spring force from its value when the bar is in the mean (static) position = spring stiffness times extension

$$= S \cdot x \cdot \theta, \text{ if } \theta \text{ is small},$$

$$= 10 \times 3 \times 12 \, \theta = 360 \, \theta \text{ lb}.$$

Torque on bar due to this is $360 \, \theta \times 3 = 1080 \, \theta$ lb ft and ignoring the small changes in torque due to weight of bar, the spring torque will be the resultant torque. Thus

$$I \cdot \frac{d^2\theta}{dt^2} + 1080 \, \theta = 0.$$

But I (about pivot) $= \dfrac{70}{32 \cdot 2} \times \dfrac{10^2}{3}$ slugs ft^2

and so

$$\frac{d^2\theta}{dt^2} + \frac{1080 \times 32 \cdot 2 \times 3}{70 \times 100} \cdot \theta = 0$$

hence

$$f_N = \frac{1}{2\pi} \sqrt{\frac{1080 \times 32 \cdot 2 \times 3}{70 \times 100}} \text{ vib/sec} = \mathbf{36 \cdot 9 \text{ vib/min}}.$$

If the bar is at θ to the static position as shown in Fig. 13.6, then there will be a change of torque due to the weight, i.e. centre of gravity moves, as well as that due to the spring force change.

Change of torque due to weight $= W \times BC = W \times AB \cos \alpha$

$$= W \times \frac{L}{2} . \theta . \cos \alpha, \text{ if } \theta \text{ small.}$$

This change of torque aids that due to the spring and thus total torque change $= 1080 \times \theta$ (for spring) $+ 70 \times 5 \times 0.707 \times \theta$ (for weight)

$$= 1080 \times \theta + 247 \times \theta = 1327 \times \theta \text{ lb ft.}$$

Hence

$$\frac{\mathrm{d}^2\theta}{\mathrm{d}t^2} + \frac{1327}{I} \times \theta = 0$$

and thus

$$f_N = 36.9 \sqrt{\frac{1327}{1080}} \text{ (by proportion)} = \textbf{41 vib/min.}$$

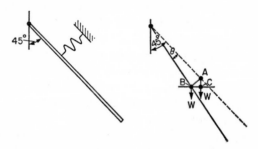

Fig. 13.6. Vibrating system of worked example 13.2

13.4. Natural Torsional Vibrations of a Two-Rotor System

The system shown in Fig. 13.7 consists of a rotor of inertia I_1

representing, for example, a single cylinder engine connected by a shaft of stiffness q_1 to a rotor I_2 which could represent a load driven by the engine. Let the two rotors be twisted angularly in

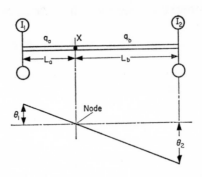

FIG. 13.7. Torsional vibrations of two-rotor system

opposite directions and released. The system now performs natural vibrations, each rotor having an angular motion about the mean position. The ends of the shaft will be twisted the same amount as the rotors attached to them and, as a result, the shaft provides a torsional elastic spring. It should be noted that the shaft ends have to move in opposite directions with the same frequency for the motion to continue periodically. At some point along the shaft there will be no relative twisting and this point, X in Fig. 13.7, is called a node. The shaft could be imagined *fixed* at the node with portions on either side vibrating freely.

Let the node divide the shaft, of diameter d, into lengths L_a and and L_b giving stiffnesses q_a and q_b. Then on either side of the node are single degree of freedom systems having the same natural frequency given by,

$$f_N = \frac{1}{2\pi} \sqrt{\frac{q_a}{I_1}} = \frac{1}{2\pi} \sqrt{\frac{q_b}{I_2}}.$$

But for a circular section shaft,

$$q_a = \frac{G \cdot J}{L_a} \text{ and } q_b = \frac{G \cdot J}{L_b}$$

and so

$$f_N = \frac{1}{2\pi} \sqrt{\frac{G \cdot J}{I_1 L_a}} = \frac{1}{2\pi} \sqrt{\frac{G \cdot J}{I_2 L_b}} \qquad (13.11)$$

and the node position is given by

$$I_1 L_a = I_2 L_b. \qquad (13.12)$$

Thus for a given system in which I_1, I_2 and $L_a + L_b = L$ is known, equation (13.12) can be used to find the position of the node and then substitution of either L_a or L_b into equation (13.11) will give the frequency.

The amplitude of the ends of the shaft will vary linearly from θ_1 at one end to zero at the node and then from zero to θ_2 in the opposite sense, as shown in Fig. 13.7. The straight line is often called the elastic line for the shaft.

13.5. Equivalent Torsional Elastic System

The method outlined in section 13.4 applies only to a shaft of uniform stiffness, i.e. constant diameter. Sometimes, however, a torsional system is such that the elastic stiffness of the shaft connecting the rotors has various values, such as the stepped shaft shown in Fig. 13.8.

Analysis can then be carried out in the manner outlined, provided the stepped shaft is replaced by an equivalent shaft of uniform stiffness, as shown in Fig. 13.8.

The two shafts will be torsionally equivalent provided they have the same overall angle of twist for a given applied torque. Thus,

$$\theta_e = \theta_1 + \theta_2 + \theta_3 + \theta_4,$$

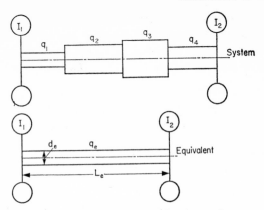

FIG. 13.8. Equivalent torsional system

where suffix e refers to the equivalent shaft and 1, 2, 3, 4 to the portions shown in Fig. 13.8.

But $\theta = T/q$, hence,

$$\frac{T}{q_e} = \frac{T}{q_1} + \frac{T}{q_2} + \frac{T}{q_3} + \frac{T}{q_4}$$

or

$$\frac{1}{q_e} = \frac{1}{q_1} + \frac{1}{q_2} + \frac{1}{q_3} + \frac{1}{q_4}. \qquad (13.13)$$

Using equation (13.13), the value of q_e is calculated and then a suitable diameter d_e selected for which there will be a corresponding length L_e. The determination of the natural frequency then follows the method of section 13.4.

WORKED EXAMPLE (U.L.2. EXT. 1938)

13.3. The flywheel of an engine driving a dynamo weighs 400 lb and has a radius of gyration of 12 in. The shaft at the flywheel end has an effective length of 10 in., and is 2 in. in diameter. The armature weighs 250 lb and its radius of gyration is 9 in.

The dynamo shaft is $1\frac{3}{4}$ in. in diameter and 8 in. in effective length. Neglecting the inertia of the coupling and of the shaft itself, calculate the natural frequency of torsional oscillations and the position of the node. Take $G = 12 \times 10^6$ lb/in².

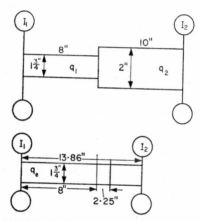

FIG. 13.9. Torsional system of worked example 13.3

SOLUTION

Referring to Fig. 13.9 and using the notation of equation (13.13),

$$\frac{1}{q_e} = \frac{1}{q_1} + \frac{1}{q_2} \quad \text{or} \quad q_e = \frac{q_1 q_2}{q_1 + q_2}$$

and so

$$q_e = \frac{G^2 J_1 J_2 / L_1 L_2}{G (J_1/L_1 + J_2/L_2)} = \frac{12 \times 10^6 \times 1 \cdot 75^4 \times 2^4}{8 \times 10 \, [(1 \cdot 75^4/8) + (2^4/10)]}$$

$$= 0 \cdot 797 \times 10^6 \text{ lb in/rad.}$$

Thus L_e for $1\frac{3}{4}$ in. diameter shaft (d_e) is

$$\frac{12 \times 10^6 \times \pi}{32} \times \frac{1 \cdot 75^4}{0 \cdot 797} = 13 \cdot 86 \text{ in.}$$

For position of node on equivalent shaft,

$$I_1 L_a = I_2 L_b \quad \text{or} \quad \frac{250}{32 \cdot 2} \times \left(\frac{3}{4}\right)^2 \times L_a = \frac{400}{32 \cdot 2} \times 1^2 \, (13 \cdot 86 - L_a),$$

since

$$L_b = 13 \cdot 86 - L_a \quad \text{and so} \quad 0 \cdot 352 L_a = 13 \cdot 86 - L_a \quad \text{giving}$$

$$L_a = 10 \cdot 25 \text{ in.}$$

The node position on the original shaft is required. The first 8 in. of the 10·25 in. corresponds with the 8 in. portion of the original shaft, leaving a further 2·25 in. of equivalent shaft. The length corresponding to this on original shaft is obtained by proportion since 5·86 in. of equivalent shaft is the same as 10 in. of 2 in. diameter shaft.

Thus length of 2 in. diameter shaft corresponding to 2·25 in. of 1·75 in. shaft is

$$\frac{2 \cdot 25}{5 \cdot 86} \times 10 = 3 \cdot 84 \text{ in.}$$

Thus node is $8 + 3 \cdot 84 = 11 \cdot 84$ in. from the armature or 6·16 in. from the flywheel.

The frequency is given by

$$f_N = \frac{1}{2\pi} \sqrt{\frac{G \cdot J}{I_1 L_a}}$$

$$= \frac{1}{2\pi} \sqrt{\frac{12 \times 10^6 \times 144 \times 1 \cdot 75^4 \times 32 \cdot 2 \times 12}{32 \times 144 \times 144 \times 250 \times 0 \cdot 75^2 \times 10 \cdot 25}}$$

$$= 22 \cdot 8 \text{ vib/sec.}$$

Worked Example (U.L.2. Ext. 1941)

13.4. The flywheel of an engine driving a dynamo weighs 300 lb and has a radius of gyration of 10 in.; the armature weighs 220 lb and has a radius of gyration of 8 in. The driving shaft has an effective length of 18 in. in and is 2 in. diameter, and a spring coupling is incorporated at one end, having a stiffness of 0.25×10^6 lb in. per radian. Neglecting the inertia of the coupling and shaft, calculate the natural frequency of torsional vibration of the system.

What would be the natural frequency if the spring coupling were omitted? Take $G = 11.9 \times 10^6$ lb/in².

SOLUTION

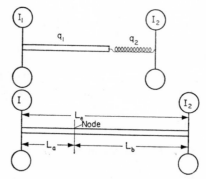

FIG. 13.10. Torsional system of worked example 13.4

Referring to Fig. 13.10 and using the notation of equation (13.13),

$$q_e = \frac{q_1 q_2}{q_1 + q_2} \text{ but } q_1 = G . J_1/L_1 = \frac{11.9 \times 10^6 \, \pi \times 2^2}{32 \times 18}$$

$$= 1.05 \times 10^6 \text{ lb in/rad.}$$

$$q_2 = 0.25 \times 10^6 \text{ lb in/rad.}$$

$$q_e = \frac{0.25 \times 1.05 \times 10^{12}}{1.30 \times 10^6} = 0.2 \times 10^6 \text{ lb in/rad.}$$

Length of equivalent shaft having 2 in. diameter is

$$L_e = \frac{1 \cdot 05}{0 \cdot 2} \times 18 = 94 \cdot 5 \text{ in.}$$

For position of node on equivalent shaft,

$$I_1 L_a = I_2 L_b \quad \text{or} \quad \frac{300}{32 \cdot 2} \times \left(\frac{10}{12}\right)^2 . L_a = \frac{220}{32 \cdot 2} \times \left(\frac{8}{12}\right)^2 . L_b,$$

giving

$$2 \cdot 13 \, L_a = L_b = 94 \cdot 5 - L_a$$

$$L_a = \frac{94 \cdot 5}{3 \cdot 13} = 30 \cdot 2 \text{ in.}$$

Hence frequency is

$$f_N = \frac{1}{2\pi} \sqrt{\frac{11 \cdot 9 \times 10^6 \times 144 \times \pi \times 2^4 \times 32 \cdot 2 \times 12^2 \times 12}{32 \times 12^4 \times 300 \times 10^2 \times 30 \cdot 2}}$$

working in feet units.

$$f_N = \textbf{14·3 vib/sec} \text{ or } \textbf{860 vib/min.}$$

Without the coupling,

$$\frac{300}{32 \cdot 2} \times \left(\frac{10}{12}\right)^2 L_a = \frac{220}{32 \cdot 2} \times \left(\frac{8}{12}\right)^2 (18 - L_a)$$

giving

$$L_a = 5 \cdot 75 \text{ in.}$$

Hence

$$f_N = 860 \sqrt{\frac{30 \cdot 2}{5 \cdot 75}} = \textbf{1945 vib/min.}$$

13.6. Natural Vibrations of Systems with Several Degrees of Freedom by Approximate Methods

With systems possessing several degrees of freedom, no

fundamentally new aspect needs consideration but the process of determining natural frequencies becomes comparatively complex. For every degree of freedom there is an equation of motion and whilst the simultaneous solution of these offers few difficulties with, say, 2 degrees of freedom, considerable work is needed when, as in vehicle ride vibrations, there can be as many as 21 degrees of freedom. This complexity is often aggravated by the complex nature of the elastic constraints connecting the masses.

Thus several methods have been evolved to cope with the complexities, use of influence numbers to specify elasticity, concept of impedance to facilitate setting up the equations of motion, analogue representation and subsequent computor solution, many methods of mathematical guessing, to name a few.

The general treatment of systems with many degrees of freedom is beyond the scope of this book, but some consideration can be given to the case of masses connected together in some simple elastic manner, such as a vibrating beam. A beam consists of many small masses each of which may have motion relative to the others, the system thus exhibiting several degrees of freedom with several modes of vibration and as many natural frequencies of transverse vibration. This is shown in Fig. 13.11 for the fundamental (1st harmonic) with all masses vibrating in phase,

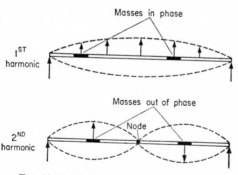

Fig. 13.11. Modes of transverse vibration

and for the second harmonic with some masses in phase and the others out of phase, there being a position of zero amplitude at a point called a *node*.

Three methods are in common use for the determination of natural transverse frequencies of a vibrating beam; the energy method based on the work of Rayleigh, the fundamental beam equation and Dunkerley's Empirical Equation.

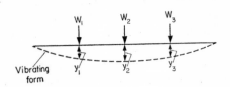

FIG. 13.12. Vibrating system for "energy method"

(a) Energy Method

The beam, as shown in Fig. 13.12, together with any loading carried is imagined to consist of a large number of concentrated masses of weights, W_1, W_2, W_3, etc., vibrating so that the maximum deformation, i.e. amplitude, is y_1, y_2, y_3, etc.

Since during the vibration there will be a continuous interchange of kinetic and elastic strain energies, the maximum values of these can be equated for natural (without losses) vibrations. The total maximum strain energy $\propto \frac{1}{2}W_1y_1 + \frac{1}{2}W_2y_2 + \frac{1}{2}W_3y_3$, etc.

$$= \sum \tfrac{1}{2} kWy. \qquad (13.14)$$

The total maximum kinetic energy

$$\frac{W_1 v_1^2}{2g} + \frac{W_2 v_2^2}{2g} + \frac{W_3 v_3^2}{2g}, \text{ etc.,}$$

$$= \sum \frac{W \cdot v^2}{2g} \qquad (13.15)$$

where v is the maximum velocity of a mass during its motion. If the motion of a mass is assumed to be simple harmonic, then its maximum velocity is given (see Chapter 4) by

$$v = \omega_N \times \text{amplitude} = \omega_N \cdot y.$$

Thus maximum kinetic energy $= \displaystyle\sum W \cdot y^2 \cdot \frac{\omega_N^2}{2g}$

and hence $\dfrac{\omega_N^2}{2g} \displaystyle\sum W \cdot y^2 = \tfrac{1}{2} \displaystyle\sum k W \cdot y$

or

$$\omega_N = \sqrt{\frac{g \, \Sigma \, k \, W \cdot y}{\Sigma \, W \cdot y^2}} \quad \text{or} \quad f_N = \frac{1}{2\pi} \sqrt{\frac{g \, \Sigma \, k \, W \cdot y}{\Sigma \, W \cdot y^2}}. \qquad (13.16)$$

If, therefore, the exact amplitude of each mass is known, the frequency may be accurately determined. However, Rayleigh showed that the calculated value does not vary much for many assumed vibrating shapes such as sine curve, parabola, etc. Consequently, the vibrating form is usually assumed to be similar to the static deflected form of the beam carrying the loads W_1, W_2, W_3, etc. Thus $k = 1$, giving

$$f_N = \frac{1}{2\pi} \sqrt{\frac{g \, \Sigma \, W \cdot \delta}{\Sigma \, W \cdot \delta^2}},$$

and if the static deflection δ, under each load is in *inches*, then the frequency is given by

$$f_N = 187 \cdot 8 \sqrt{\frac{\Sigma \, W \cdot \delta}{\Sigma \, W \cdot \delta^2}} \text{ vib/min.} \qquad (13.17)$$

Note that the beam mass can be included as a number of concentrated loads.

In the case of a beam carrying a uniform loading,

$$f_N = 187\cdot8 \sqrt{\frac{\int_0^L \delta \cdot dx}{\int_0^L \delta^2 \cdot dx}},$$

and for a freely supported beam carrying a uniform load over its span,

$$f_N = \frac{211\cdot8}{\sqrt{\delta_s}} \text{ vib/min.}$$

where δ_s is the static deflection in inches at mid-span.

(b) Fundamental Beam Equation

When the beam is vibrating, it may be considered at any instant to be in dynamic equilibrium under the action of the elastic forces arising from its displacement and those due to its inertia. Thus the inertia forces are considered to give a rate of loading on the beam which, if statically applied, would deform the beam to its vibrating position.

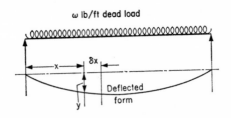

Fig. 13.13. Vibrating system for "beam equation"

Figure 13.13 shows an element of the beam over which the rate of loading, due to inertia, is w.

$$\text{Inertia load on element} = \frac{w}{g} \cdot \delta x \cdot \frac{\partial^2 y}{\partial t^2}.$$

But from simple beam theory, the rate of loading is $E \cdot I \cdot (\partial^4 y / \partial x^4)$. Thus

$$E \cdot I \cdot \frac{\partial^4 y}{\partial x^4} \cdot \delta x = - \frac{w}{g} \cdot \delta x \cdot \frac{\partial^2 y}{\partial t^2}$$

or

$$\frac{\partial^4 y}{\partial x^4} + \frac{w}{g \cdot E \cdot I} \cdot \frac{\partial^2 y}{\partial t^2} = 0. \tag{13.18}$$

Equation (13.18), is called the fundamental beam equation which has a simple solution *only* for the case of beams carrying uniform loading and with the assumption of simple harmonic motion. In view of the restricted practical value the equation will not be developed any further. It can be shown that for a freely supported beam carrying a uniformly distributed load, the frequency is given by

$$f_N = \frac{211 \cdot 4}{\sqrt{\delta_s}} \text{ vib/min.} \tag{13.19}$$

if δ_s is the static deflection in inches at mid-span.

Also, for such a loaded beam *only*, the 2nd, 3rd, etc., harmonic frequencies are related to the first in the following simple manner:

$$\text{2nd} = \text{1st} \times 2^2$$

$$\text{3rd} = \text{1st} \times 3^2, \text{ etc.}$$

(c) *Dunkerley's Empirical Equation*

For this equation, each load carried by the beam is imagined to be applied separately and the frequency due to that load only is calculated. The method for a beam carrying three concentrated loads together with a distributed load (including its own weight), as shown in Fig. 13.14, is as follows.

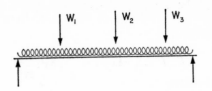

FIG. 13.14. Vibrating system for Dunkerley Equation

For a single concentrated load W_1 only on the beam,

$$f_1 = \frac{187 \cdot 8}{\sqrt{\delta_1}}.$$

δ_1 is the deflection at point where W_1 is applied and due to W_1 only.

Similarly, $\qquad f_2 = 187 \cdot 8/\sqrt{\delta_2}, f_3 = 187 \cdot 8/\sqrt{\delta_3}.$

For the distributed load only, $f_s = 211 \cdot 4/\sqrt{\delta_s}$, where δ_s is the static deflection at mid-span.

Then the frequency of vibration for the completely loaded beam is given by

$$\frac{1}{f_N^2} = \frac{1}{f_1^2} + \frac{1}{f_2^2} + \frac{1}{f_3^2} + \cdots \frac{1}{f_s^2}.$$

This equation, called Dunkerley's Equation, can be put into a more practical form such as

$$f_N = \frac{187 \cdot 8}{\sqrt{\delta_1 + \delta_2 + \delta_3 + (\delta_s/1 \cdot 27)}} \quad \text{vib/min,} \quad (13.20)$$

if the appropriate static deflections are in inches.

WORKED EXAMPLES (U.L.2. EXT. 1950. (Modified)).

13.5. Calculate the lowest frequency of transverse vibration of a steel shaft 2 in. in diameter and 10 ft long carrying a wheel weighing 60 lb at 2 ft from one end and one weighing 40 lb at 3 ft from the other end. The shaft may be considered simply supported on bearings at the ends. Density of steel 0·285 lb/in³. E for steel $= 30 \times 10^6$ lb/in².

SOLUTION

(a) Using Dunkerley's Method.

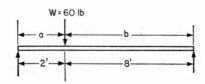

FIG. 13.15. Loaded beam of worked example 13.5

Figure 13.15 shows the beam carrying the 60 lb load only. The deflection at the load is given by $(W \cdot a^2 b^2/3 \cdot EI \cdot L)$, and thus

$$\delta_{60} = \frac{60 \times 24^2 \times 96^2 \times 64}{3 \times 30 \times 10^6 \times \pi \times 2^4 \times 120} = 0·0375 \text{ in.}$$

Similarly, for the 40 lb load

$$\delta_{40} = \frac{40 \times 36^2 \times 84^2 \times 64}{3 \times 30 \times 10^6 \times \pi \times 2^4 \times 120} = 0·041 \text{ in.}$$

Weight of beam itself $= (\pi/4) \times 2^2 \times 120 \times 0.285 = 107$ lb. Deflection at mid-span due to its own weight

$$= \delta_s = \frac{5}{384} \cdot \frac{W \cdot L^3}{EI},$$

and thus

$$\delta_s = \frac{5 \times 107 \times 120^3 \times 64}{384 \times 30 \times 10^6 \times \pi \times 2^4} = 0·102 \text{ in.}$$

By Dunkerley's Equation (modified),

$$f_N = \frac{187 \cdot 8}{\sqrt{0 \cdot 0375 + 0 \cdot 041 + (0 \cdot 102/1 \cdot 27)}} = \textbf{469 vib/min.}$$

(b) By the Energy Method.

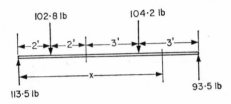

FIG. 13.16. Loaded beam of worked example 13.5

The beam is considered fully loaded and the mass of the beam itself has to be included. Whilst, in practice, this might mean the dividing of the beam into many *concentrated* loads, this would give a solution too long for examination purposes. Here, therefore, to allow for the beam mass, parts of the beam weight are included with the concentrated loads. There is a 4 ft length of beam (2 ft on either side of the 60 lb load), which can be added to the 60 lb load giving, as shown in Fig. 13.16, a load of 102·8 lb. Similarly, the 40 lb load is at the centre of the remaining 6 ft of the beam and the weight of that part of the beam can be added to the 40 lb load giving a load of 104·2 lb.

The beam reactions now become 113·5 lb and 93·5 lb as shown and the static deflections can be calculated. Macaulay's Method is used here.

$$EI \cdot \frac{d^2y}{dx^2} = -113 \cdot 5 \cdot x + 102 \cdot 8\,[x - 2] + 104 \cdot 2\,[x - 7]$$

$$EI \cdot \frac{dy}{dx} = -56 \cdot 75x^2 + 51 \cdot 4\,[x - 2]^2 + 52 \cdot 1\,[x - 7]^2 + A$$

$$EI . y = - 18.92x^3 + 17.1 [x - 2]^3 + 17.4 [x - 7]^3 + A . x + B.$$

The end conditions are,

> when $x = 0$, $y = 0$ giving $B = 0$ and
> when $x = 10$, $y = 0$ thus

$$0 = - 18{,}920 + 8750 + 470 + 10A \text{ and so, } A = 970.$$

Deflection at 102·8 lb load

$$= (- 18.92 \times 8 + 970 \times 2)/EI = 1789/EI$$
$$= 0.131 \text{ in. (care with units).}$$

Deflection at 104·2 lb load

$$= (- 18.92 \times 343 + 17.1 \times 125 + 7 \times 970)/EI$$
$$= 2430/EI = 0.177 \text{ in.}$$

$\Sigma W . \delta = (102.8 \times 0.131) + (104.2 \times 0.177) = 31.9$
$\Sigma W . \delta^2 = (102.8 \times 0.131^2) + (104.2 \times 0.177^2) = 5.02$

giving

$$f_N = 187.8 \sqrt{\frac{\Sigma W . \delta}{\Sigma W . \delta^2}} = 187.8 \sqrt{\frac{31.9}{5.02}} = \textbf{472 vib/min.}$$

13.7 Forced, Single Degree of Freedom, Undamped Vibrations

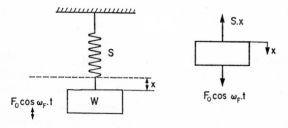

Fig. 13.17. Vibrating system subjected to periodic force

Figure 13.17 shows the mass elastic system considered in section 13.3 representing a single degree of longitudinal freedom.

A periodic disturbance is applied to the vibrating mass. This situation arises in engine mounting where there is an unbalanced force in the line of reciprocation. We shall specify the periodic force as $F = F_0 \cos \omega_F t$, so that its maximum value if F_0 and its frequency $= \omega_F/2\pi$, the suffix F referring to forced conditions.

For the position of the vibrating mass shown in Fig. 13.17, the forces acting are (additional to those at static position); spring force $= S \cdot x$, acting upwards, and a disturbing force $F_0 \cos \omega_F t$. Thus the equation of motion of the mass is,

$$F_0 \cos \omega_F t - S \cdot x = \frac{W}{g} \cdot \frac{d^2 x}{dt^2} \quad (x \text{ downwards})$$

giving

$$\frac{W}{g} \cdot \frac{d^2 x}{dt^2} + S \cdot x = F_0 \cos \omega_F t \qquad (13.21)$$

This equation can be written as,

$$\frac{d^2 x}{dt^2} + b \cdot x = c \cdot \cos \omega_F t \qquad (13.22)$$

where $b = S \cdot g/W$ and $c = F_0 \cdot g/W$.

The full solution to equation (13.22) is

$$x = \underset{\text{(transient)}}{A \cdot \sin \sqrt{b}\, t + B \cdot \cos \sqrt{b}\, t} + \underset{\text{(steady state)}}{\frac{c}{b - \omega_F^2} \cdot \cos \omega_F t.} \qquad (13.23)$$

The solution consists of a term representing a natural vibration, which is normally transient in character and which in practical mechanical circumstances would die away due to damping present, and a steady state term. If, therefore, the position of the mass is required shortly after the application of a forced disturbance, the full solution is needed, but if steady conditions are arrived at, then the solution is

$$x = \frac{c}{b - \omega_F^2} \cdot \cos \omega_F t. \qquad (13.24)$$

Equation (13.24) indicates that the frequency of forced vibrations is the same as that of the forcing disturbance, i.e.

$$f_F = \frac{1}{t_F} = \frac{\omega_F}{2\pi}.$$

The amplitude of the motion of the mass is

$$x_0 = \frac{c}{b - \omega_F^2}. \tag{13.25}$$

Equation (13.25) is the form which students will find most useful for solving examination problems, but equation (13.25) may be modified by substituting the physical quantities for b and c, and this leads to the equation

$$x_0 = \frac{F_0/S}{1 - (\omega_F^2/\omega_N)^2}$$

If, however, a force of magnitude F_0 were applied *statically* to the mass, a static deflection of $\delta = F_0/S$ would be obtained and so

$$x_0 = \delta \cdot \frac{1}{1 - (\omega_F/\omega_N)^2} = \delta \cdot D, \quad \text{where } D = \frac{1}{1 - (\omega_F/\omega_N)^2},$$

is called a dynamic magnifier, i.e. the static deflection $\delta = F_0/S$, is magnified by the forced disturbance.

The amplitude of the forced vibration will, for a given system of W and S, depend on the value of the forcing frequency, and a convenient way of representing this is to plot a curve of $x_0/\delta = D$ against the frequency ratio $\omega_F/\omega_N = f_F/f_N$. Figure 13.18 shows a typical curve. (Note that the equation for values of $\omega_F/\omega_N > 1$ gives a negative value for D; this indicates a change of phase of 180° (between mass and forcing), but the graph (to save paper) is plotted as though it were positive.)

When $\omega_F = \omega_N$, i.e. forcing and system natural frequencies are

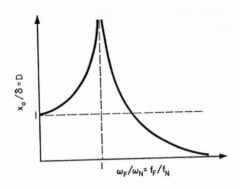

FIG. 13.18. Response curve for system of Fig. 13.17

the same, the amplitude of vibration is theoretically infinitely large. In practice, the amplitude is limited by damping but nevertheless can be too large for safety. This condition, called *resonance*, is generally to be avoided. However, if the system can be run so that $\omega_F > \omega_N$ the amplitude of vibration becomes small. This principle is utilised in turbines where critical resonant speeds are avoided.

WORKED EXAMPLE (U.L.2. EXT. 1950)

13.6. A vertical single cylinder engine weighing 1200 lb is carried on elastic floor beams whose static deflection under the weight of the engine is 0·38 in. Calculate the frequency of free vibrations in a vertical plane. The engine is now run at 130 rev/min. The reciprocating parts weigh 100 lb., the stroke is 7 in. and length of connecting rod is 14 in. Calculate the vertical movement of the engine due to (a) lack of primary balance, (b) lack of secondary balance.

SOLUTION

The system is that of Fig. 13.17.

$$\text{Natural frequency} = \frac{187\cdot8}{\sqrt{0\cdot38}} = 304 \text{ vib/min.}$$

(a) Primary inertia force $= (W/g) \cdot r \cdot \omega_F^2 \cos \theta$, with ω_F = engine speed in rad/sec.

$$\text{Force } F = \frac{100}{32\cdot2} \times \frac{3\cdot5}{12} \times \left(\frac{130}{60} \times 2\pi\right)^2 \cos\left[\left(\frac{130}{60} \times 2\pi\right) \cdot t\right] \text{ lb}$$

$$= 167\cdot5 \cos 13\cdot6\, t \text{ lb.}$$

Amplitude of motion $= \dfrac{c}{b - \omega_F^2}$

where

$$c = F_0\, g/W, \quad \text{b} = Sg/W = g/\delta,$$

$$c = \frac{167\cdot5 \times 32\cdot2}{1200} = 4\cdot5, \quad \text{and} \quad b = g/\delta = \frac{32\cdot2 \times 12}{0\cdot38} = 1015.$$

Hence amplitude $= \dfrac{4\cdot5}{1015 - 13\cdot6^2}$ ft $= \dfrac{4\cdot5 \times 12}{830}$ in. $= 0\cdot065$ in.

Total movement (between extreme positions) = **0·13 in.**

(b) Secondary inertia force $= \dfrac{W}{g} \cdot \dfrac{r\omega^2}{n} \cos 2\,\omega_F t$

$$= 41\cdot9 \cos 2\,\omega_F t.$$

The solution of the differential equation
$$(\text{d}^2x/\text{d}t^2) + b \cdot x = c \cdot \cos 2\,\omega_F t$$
is given by

$$x_0 = \frac{c}{b - (2\,\omega_F)^2} = \frac{4\cdot5}{1015 - 27\cdot2^2} \times 12 \text{ in.}$$

$$= 0\cdot049 \text{ in.}$$

Total movement = **0·098 in.**

WORKED EXAMPLE (U.L.2. EXT. 1946)

13.7. The time of free vibration of a mass hung from the end of a helical spring is 0·8 sec. When the mass is stationary the upper end is made to move upwards with a displacement $y = 1 \cdot 8 \sin 2\pi t$ inches. Neglecting the mass of the spring and any damping, determine the vertical distance through which the mass has moved in the first 0·3 sec.

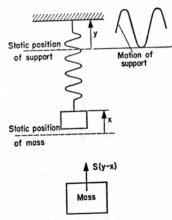

FIG. 13.19. Vibrating system subjected to periodic displacement

SOLUTION

In this particular problem the disturbing force is applied to the spring support and not directly to the mass. Let the support, as shown in Fig. 13.19, be a distance y above the static position and the corresponding displacement of the mass be x.

The force acting on the mass is the spring force due to the *relative* movement of the spring ends $= S(y - x)$, and the equation of motion of the mass is

$$S(y - x) = \frac{W}{g} \cdot \frac{\mathrm{d}^2 x}{\mathrm{d}t^2}$$

or,

$$\frac{d^2x}{dt^2} + \frac{S \cdot g}{W} \cdot x = \frac{S \cdot g}{W} \cdot y, \quad \text{but } y = y_0 \sin \omega_F t,$$

thus

$$\frac{d^2x}{dt^2} + \frac{S \cdot g}{W} \cdot x = \frac{S \cdot g \cdot y_0}{W} \sin \omega_F t.$$

This is comparable with equation (13.22), the full solution being

$$x = A \cdot \sin \sqrt{b}t + B \cdot \cos \sqrt{b}t + \frac{c}{b - \omega_F^2} \cdot \sin \omega_F t$$

where

$$b = \omega_N^2 = \left(\frac{2\pi}{0 \cdot 8}\right)^2 = 61 \cdot 7 \quad \text{or } b = 7 \cdot 85, \ \omega_F = 2\pi;$$

$$c = b \cdot y_0 = 61 \cdot 7 \times \frac{1 \cdot 8}{12} = 9 \cdot 25,$$

and so

$$x \text{ ft} = A \cdot \sin 7 \cdot 85t + B \cdot \cos 7 \cdot 85t + \frac{9 \cdot 25}{61 \cdot 7 - 4\pi^2} \sin 2\pi t.$$

However, the time is measured from the system in rest at the static position so that when $t = 0$ so $x = 0$ and thus, $B = 0$ and when $t = 0$, $dx/dt = 0$ and after differentiating $0 = 7 \cdot 85A + 2 \times 0 \cdot 416$, giving $A = -0 \cdot 333$. Finally, when $t = 0 \cdot 3$ sec,

$$x = -0 \cdot 333 \sin 2 \cdot 355 \text{ rad} + 0 \cdot 416 \sin 1 \cdot 8 \text{ rad}$$
$$= -4 \times 0 \cdot 7 + 5 \times 0 \cdot 95 \text{ in.} = \mathbf{1 \cdot 95 \text{ in.}}$$

13.8. Whirling of Shafts

Owing to imperfections of manufacture, to static deflections, or to the eccentric mounting of rotors, etc., a shaft will rarely rotate with its mass centre on the line joining its bearing centres but will whirl round in a bow, like a skipping rope. If the speed of such a shaft be gradually increased, the radius of whirl will increase until at some speed the shaft becomes violently unstable and if this speed is maintained the large deflection may lead to failure. If, however, the speed be run through quickly, the shaft will become straight again and run true until at some higher speed the same effect will occur, the deflection now being in a double bow. These speeds are called critical whirling speeds.

For an explanation of observed phenomena it is necessary to consider the shaft subjected to forced damped vibrations in two directions at right angles together with a rotation, and such treatment given in Volume II is beyond the present scope. However, the following limited case can be considered.

Simple Treatment of Light Shaft carrying a Heavy Rotor

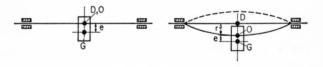

FIG. 13.20. Whirling of a shaft

Figure 13.20 shows a shaft mounted in bearings and carrying a rotor, centre of mass G, attached eccentric, by an amount e, to the shaft at O. For simplicity the static defection of the system is ignored.

When whirling, the shaft bows so that point O is a distance r from its original position D.

The rotor mass centre is rotating in a circular path of radius $(r + e)$ and the resulting centrifugal force is balanced by the elastic bending forces of the beam. If S is the beam force per unit whirl radius, r, then for a whirl velocity ω,

$$\frac{W}{g} \cdot \omega^2 (r + e) = S \cdot r$$

and so

$$r = \frac{(W/g) \cdot \omega^2 \cdot e}{S - (W/g) \cdot \omega^2} = \frac{e}{(S \cdot g ./W)(1/\omega^2) - 1}.$$

However, $S \cdot g/W = \omega_N^2$ for natural vibrations and so

$$r = \frac{e}{(\omega_N/\omega)^2 - 1}, \text{ or } r = \frac{e}{(f_N/n)^2 - 1}. \tag{13.26}$$

If, therefore, the shaft speed in rev/min (n) equals the frequency of natural transverse vibration in vib/min, the deflection becomes infinite, i.e. critical whirling speed = transverse frequency.

Notes: (i) With shaft speed less than critical, G is situated from D on the further side of O.

(ii) With shaft speed greater than critical, G lies between D and O and a speed can be reached when G coincides with D and stable running conditions prevail.

(iii) For a given whirl radius there are two speeds one on either side of the critical.

For reasons already stated, no explanation of notes (i) to (iii) is attempted, but readers should notice the similarity between equation (13.26) and the results and equations of forced vibrations.

WORKED EXAMPLE (U.L.2 EXT. 1952)

13.8. A light shaft of 0·5 in. diameter freely supported in bearings 4 ft apart carries a single central load of 1·0 lb. This single load has to be replaced by two loads of W lb each symmetrically set 1 ft from the respective bearings and between them. Determine the magnitude of these two loads for the first whirling speed to be unaltered, and estimate (a) the first whirling speed, (b) the second whirling speed for the two load system. $E = 30 \times 10^6$ lb/in².

SOLUTION

Deflection due to the central $1 \cdot 0$ lb load $= (W \cdot L^3/48 \cdot EI)$

$$= \frac{1 \times 48^3 \times 64}{48 \times 30 \times 10^6 \times \pi \times 0 \cdot 5^4} = 0 \cdot 025 \text{ in.}$$

First critical whirling speed $=$ first natural transverse frequency

$$= \frac{187 \cdot 8}{\sqrt{0 \cdot 025}} = \frac{187 \cdot 8}{0 \cdot 158} = \textbf{1185 rev/min.}$$

For the two load system and using Dunkerley's Method, deflection under W lb due to that load

$$= \frac{W \cdot a^2 b^2}{3 \times EI \cdot L} = \frac{W \times 12^2 \times 36^2 \times 64}{3 \times 30 \times 10^6 \times \pi \times 0 \cdot 5^4 \times 48}$$

$$= 0 \cdot 014 W \text{ in.}$$

Hence

$$f_N = \frac{187 \cdot 8}{\sqrt{0 \cdot 014 W + 0 \cdot 014 W}} = \frac{187 \cdot 8}{\sqrt{0 \cdot 028 W}}$$

and for this to be unaltered,

$$\frac{187 \cdot 8}{\sqrt{0 \cdot 028 W}} = \frac{187 \cdot 8}{\sqrt{0 \cdot 025}}.$$

Hence

$$W = \frac{0 \cdot 025}{0 \cdot 028} = \textbf{0 \cdot 89 lb.}$$

For the second whirling speed, the deflected form of the beam is shown in Fig. 13.21.

The system has the same frequency as that of a load of $0 \cdot 89$ lb central on a span of 2 ft. Static deflection due to this is

$$0.025 \times 0.89 \times \frac{1}{8} = 0.0028 \text{ in.}$$

Second whirling speed $= \dfrac{187.8}{\sqrt{0.0028}} = $ **3550 rev/min.**

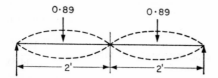

FIG. 13.21. Whirling shaft of worked example 13.8

The corresponding values using Energy Method are $W = $ **1 lb**, and second whirling speed = **3550 rev/min.**

WORKED EXAMPLE

13.9. A light shaft of $\frac{1}{2}$ in. diameter is supported in spherical bearings 20 in. apart. A disc weighing 32 lb is attached at mid-span but with an eccentricity of 0·02 in. If the bending stress in the shaft due to whirling of the disc is not to exceed 18,000 lb/in², find the speed range within which the shaft should not be run. Assume $E = 30 \times 10$ lb/in².

SOLUTION

The maximum bending moment allowable

$$= p \cdot I/y = \frac{18{,}000 \times \pi \times 0.5^4}{64 \times 0.25} \text{ lb in.}$$

This is caused by a central load W_1, thus,

$$\frac{W_1 \times 20}{4} = \frac{18{,}000 \times \pi \times 0.5^4}{64 \times 0.25} \quad \text{and so } W_1 = 44.2 \text{ lb.}$$

Radius of whirl caused by this maximum allowable load

$$= \frac{W_1 L^3}{48 . EI} = \frac{44 \cdot 2 \times 20^3 \times 64}{48 \times 30 \times 10^6 \times \pi \times 0 \cdot 5^4} = 0 \cdot 080 \text{ in.}$$

Static deflection of shaft due to disc weight $= 0 \cdot 08 \times \dfrac{32}{44 \cdot 2}$

$$= 0 \cdot 058 \text{ in.}$$

Natural transverse frequency of vibration $= \dfrac{187 \cdot 8}{\sqrt{0 \cdot 058}}$

$$= 780 \text{ vib/min.}$$

Thus

$$\pm 0 \cdot 08 = \frac{0 \cdot 02}{(780/n)^2 - 1}$$

or

$$\left(\frac{780}{n}\right)^2 = 1 \pm \frac{0 \cdot 2}{0 \cdot 8} = 1 \cdot 25 \text{ or } 0 \cdot 75$$

giving

$$n = \mathbf{696} \text{ or } \mathbf{901} \text{ rev/min.}$$

13.9. Natural, Viscous Damped, Single Degree of Freedom Vibrations

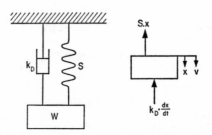

Fig. 13.22. Vibrating system subjected to viscous damping

The system considered, and shown in Fig. 13.22, is a spring–mass single degree of freedom, one with a viscous force, shown by a damper, applied to the mass. The viscous force F_D, is proportional to the rate of shearing a viscous fluid and so, $F_D = k_D \cdot (dx/dt)$, where k_D is called the viscous damping coefficient (lb/ft/sec). The equation of motion is

$$-S \cdot x - k_D \cdot \frac{dx}{dt} = \frac{W}{g} \cdot \frac{d^2x}{dt^2}$$

or

$$\frac{W}{g} \cdot \frac{d^2x}{dt^2} + k_D \cdot \frac{dx}{dt} + S \cdot x = 0$$

giving

$$\frac{d^2x}{dt^2} + a \cdot \frac{dx}{dt} + b \cdot x = 0 \qquad (13.27)$$

where

$$a = k_D \cdot g/W \qquad \text{and} \qquad b = S \cdot g/W.$$

Solution to equation (13.27) depends on the relative values of a and b, and if

(i) $a^2 > 4b$, the system is so heavily damped that it moves slowly back to its original position after a disturbance, i.e. the system is dead beat;

(ii) $a^2 < 4b$, a true damped vibration occurs; and

(iii) $a^2 = 4b$, represents a transition state from the dead beat to the damped vibration and is called *critical damping*.

For case (ii), the solution to equation (13.27) is

$$x = e^{(-a \cdot t/2)} [A \cdot \sin \sqrt{b - (a/2)^2}\, t + B \cdot \cos \sqrt{b - (a/2)^2}\, t] \quad (13.28).$$

The solution is in two parts. The first, $e^{(-a \cdot t/2)}$, represents the decreasing effect of the damping on the amplitude of vibration as time increases. The other part, in brackets, represents a natural vibration whose frequency is for most practical mechanical cases only slightly different to the undamped case. The solution is shown graphically in Fig. 13.23.

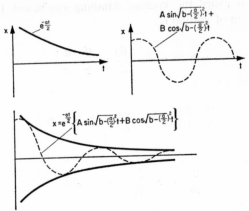

FIG. 13.23. Response curves for system of Fig. 13.22

Frequency of Damped Vibration. From the solution for the damped motion, equation (13.28), the periodic time of damped vibration is

$$t_D = \frac{2\pi}{\sqrt{b - (a/2)^2}} \quad \text{and} \quad f_D = \frac{1}{2\pi}\sqrt{b - (a/2)^2}. \quad (13.29)$$

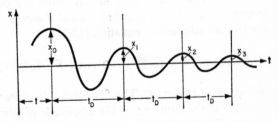

FIG. 13.24. Amplitude of damped vibration

Amplitude of Damped Vibration. Figure 13.24 shows a curve of displacement against time for a natural damped vibration in which the amplitudes of vibration, in order, *on one side* of the mean are x_0 after time t, x_1 after time $t + t_D$, x_2 after time $t + 2t_D$, etc., with t_D the periodic time of a complete vibration. From equation (13.28),

$x_0 = e^{-a \cdot t/2} [A \cdot \sin pt + B \cdot \cos pt]$ if $p = \sqrt{b - (a/2)^2}$.

$x_1 = e^{-a/2(t + t_D)} [A \cdot \sin \cdot p (t + t_D) + B \cdot \cos \cdot p (t + t_D)]$.

But if t_D is the periodic time, then $A \cdot \sin pt = A \cdot \sin p (t + t_D)$; hence,

$$\frac{x_0}{x_1} = \frac{e^{-a \cdot t/2}}{e^{-a/2(t + t_D)}} = e^{a \cdot t_D/2} = \frac{x_2}{x_3}, \text{ etc.} \quad (13.30)$$

Worked Example (U.L.2. Ext. 1951)

13.10. A mass of 10 lb hangs from a spring and makes damped vibration. The time of 50 complete vibrations is found to be 20 sec and the ratio of the first downward displacement to the sixth is found to be 2·25. Find the stiffness of the spring in lb per ft and the damping force in lb per ft per sec.

Solution

$$\frac{x_1}{x_2} = e^{a \cdot t_D/2} = \frac{x_2}{x_3} = \frac{x_3}{x_4} = \frac{x_4}{x_5} = \frac{x_5}{x_6},$$

hence

$$\frac{x_1}{x_6} = (e^{a \cdot t_D/2})^5 = 2\cdot25,$$

and so

$$2\cdot5 \, a \cdot t_D = \log_e 2\cdot25 = 0\cdot8109,$$

and

$$a \, . \, t_D = 0{\cdot}3240.$$

$$f_D = 1/t_D = \frac{50}{20} = 2{\cdot}5 = \frac{1}{2\pi} \, \sqrt{b - (a/2)^2},$$

$$25\pi^2 = b - a^2/4 \qquad \text{but} \quad a = \frac{0{\cdot}324}{t_D} = 0{\cdot}8109,$$

and so

$$a/2 = 0{\cdot}4055$$

giving

$$25\pi^2 = b - 0{\cdot}4055^2, \qquad \text{or} \qquad b = 25\pi^2 \text{ (approx.).}$$

But

$$b = g/\delta \qquad \text{and so} \qquad \delta = \frac{32{\cdot}2}{25\pi^2} = 0{\cdot}13 \text{ ft.}$$

$$\text{Stiffness of spring} = \frac{10}{0{\cdot}13} = \textbf{76 lb/ft.}$$

$$\text{Damping coefficient } k_D = a \, . \, W/g = \frac{0{\cdot}8109 \times 10}{32{\cdot}2}$$

$$= \textbf{0}{\cdot}\textbf{252 lb/ft/sec.}$$

Examples

13.11. The pendulum shown in Fig. 13.25, is suspended from a fixed pivot at O. The pendulum consists of a bar B of weight 2 lb, and a block C of weight 12 lb. The centres of gravity G_1 and G_2 of B and C are at distances 6 in. and 15 in. from O. The radii of gyration of B and C, each about its own centre of gravity, are respectively 4 in. and 1 in. A light spring is attached to the pendulum at a point P, 8 in. from O, and is anchored at a fixed point Q. When the pendulum is in equilibrium the line $OG_1 \, PG_2$ is at 45° from the vertical and the angle OPQ is 90°. The spring stretches 1 in. for each 4 lb tension.

Calculate the natural frequency of the pendulum for small oscillations about the equilibrium position.

Answer: 70 vib/min.

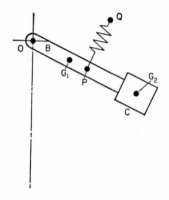

FIG. 13.25. Pendulum of example 13.11

13.12. A solid shaft AB, of 4 in. diameter, is rigidly connected at its ends to two hollow shafts AC and BD both of external diameter $5\frac{1}{2}$ in. and internal diameter $4\frac{1}{2}$ in. At C and D two masses of weight 280 lb and 550 lb, and of radius of gyration 7 in. and 15 in respectively, are attached to the ends of the hollow shafts.

Determine from first principles the frequency of free torsional vibrations, and the position of the node.

Modulus of rigidity is 12×10^6 lb/in².

Answer: 3350 vib/min; 1·16 in. from B on solid shaft.   (U.L.2. Ext. 1946)

13.13. A shaft $ABCD$ 5 ft long has flywheels at its ends A and D. Flywheel A weighs 1200 lb and has a radius of gyration of 2 ft and flywheel D weighs 1600 lb and has a radius of gyration of 3 ft.

The connecting shaft has a diameter of 2 in. for portion AB which is 15 in. long; and has a diameter of 2·5 in. for portion BC which is 20 in. long; and has a diameter d in. for portion CD which is 25 in. long.

Determine (a) the diameter d of the portion CD so that the node of torsional vibration of the system will be at the centre of the length BC; (b) the natural frequency of torsional vibrations, given that the modulus of rigidity for steel $= 12 \times 10^6$ lb/in².

Answer: (a) 3·64 in.; (b) 224 vib/min.   (U.L.2. Int. 1950)

13.14. The periodic time of free vibration of a weight hanging from a vertical spiral spring is 0·7 sec. When the weight is hanging at rest the upper end of the spring is given a vertical displacement of 3 sin 2 π . t in., t being the time in sec measured from the beginning of the motion.

(a) Calculate the height through which the weight will have risen when $t = 0.45$ sec.

(b) Explain briefly the changes which will take place in the motion of the weight if the oscillation of the upper end of the spring is continued.

Answer: (a) 4·63 in.; (b) 5·36 in.   (U.L.2. Ext. 1955)

13.15. A machine of total weight 200 lb is bolted to an elastic foundation which deflects 0·18 in. under the dead weight. In the machine is a vertical single-cylinder reciprocating engine running at 250 rev/min and having maximum out of balance primary and secondary forces of 5 lb and 1·2 lb respectively.

Calculate the maximum vertical deflection of the elastic mounting due to the combined action of the two unbalanced forces and the corresponding crank position from the top dead centre.

Answer: 0·0107 in., 180°.   (U.L.2. Int. 1956)

13.16. Explain the strain energy method of finding the whirling speed of a shaft carrying various masses.

Find the whirling speed of a 2 in. diameter steel shaft simply supported at the ends in bearings 60 in. apart carrying masses of 150 lb at 15 in. from one end, 200 lb at the centre and 250 lb at 15 in. from the other end.

$E = 30 \times 10^6$ lb/in². Ignore the mass of the shaft.

Answer: 696 rev/min (Energy), 660 rev/min (Dunkerley).   (U.L.2. Ext. 1951)

13.17. A uniform steel shaft 3·0 in. in diameter and 4 ft long carries three discs, each weighing 100 lb. The shaft is carried in bearings A and B, situated at the extreme ends of the shaft. The discs are at distances of 1 ft, 2 ft, 3 ft, respectively from bearing A. The shaft material weighs 0·29 lb/in³. and E is 29×10^6 lb/in².

Determine the first and second whirling speeds for this arrangement.

(U.L.3. Ext. 1957)

Answer: 1st 2610 rev/min (Dunkerley), 2460 rev/min (Energy); 2nd 10,600 rev/min (Dunkerley), 9760 rev/min (Energy).

13.18. A circular steel shaft AB is 2 in. in diameter and 8 ft 4 in. in length; it carries a plain disc at A of 15 in. diameter and 50 lb weight, and another disc at B of 24 in. diameter and 120 lb weight.

The shaft is held firmly at some point C such that the frequency of torsional oscillation is the same for the two sections on either side of C.

Find the frequency of *transverse* vibration of each of the above sections of the shaft.

(E for steel is 30×10^6 lb/in².).

Answer: 281 and 2750 vib/min.   (U.L.2. Ext. 1956)

13.19. (a) A load of 200 lb is suspended from a coil spring of stiffness 100 lb/in. Find the frequency of free vibration.

(b) The system is now damped: the weight is pulled downwards a definite distance and, if released, the vibration amplitude is reduced to 0·10 of the original in four complete oscillations. Determine the frequency of the damped oscillations and the value of the damping force in lb/ft/sec. Credit will be given for a proof (in outline) of the formula used in part (b).

Answer: (a) 132 vib/min; (b) 133 vib/min, 15·7 lb/ft/sec.   (U.L.2. Ext. 1952)

13.20. A rotor weighing 90 lb and having a radius of gyration of $5\frac{1}{4}$ in. is acted on, by a torque of 3000 lb in. per radian displacement of the rotor from some datum position and directed towards that datum. Calculate the frequency of free vibrations following a disturbance. A damping torque is now applied proportional to the angular velocity and having a magnitude of 30 lb in. when the angular velocity is 1 rad/sec. Write down the differential equation for this case and its solution. Evaluate the constants if at time zero the rotor is stationary with a displacement of 2° from the datum position. What is now the frequency and ratio of amplitudes of successive swings to the same side of the datum position?

Answer: 3·3 vib/sec, 0·035; 0·0036, 3·28 vib/sec, 1·9.   (U.L.2. Ext. 1952)

CHAPTER FOURTEEN

GENERAL DYNAMICS

14.1. Kinetic Energy of a Rigid Link in Plane Motion

In Chapter 1, when considering velocity diagrams for rigid links, it has been seen that the volocity of all points on a *rigid* link can be considered as that due to a common translational velocity v equal to that of the centre of mass, together with a rotational velocity ω about the centre of mass. Thus the kinetic energy of the link will consist of a part due to this common translational velocity $= (W . v^2/2g)$, and a part due to the common rotational velocity $= \frac{1}{2} I_G . \omega^2$.

$$\text{Total kinetic energy} = \frac{Wv^2}{2g} + \tfrac{1}{2} I_G . \omega^2$$

(14.1)

where I_G is the moment of inertia of the link about its centre of mass G, and W is the weight of the link.

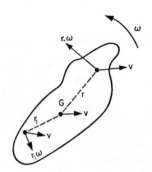

FIG. 14.1. Kinetic energy of a link

Students unfamiliar with the terms I_G, etc., should consider a particle of weight δW at a distance r from G as shown in Fig. 14.1. The components of the velocity of the particle are v and $r \cdot \omega$, giving the kinetic energy

$$= \frac{\delta W}{2g} \cdot v^2 + \frac{\delta W}{2g} (r \cdot \omega)^2 \text{ and the total kinetic energy is thus}$$

$$= \frac{v^2}{2g} \Sigma \delta W + \frac{\omega^2}{2} \sum \frac{\delta W}{g} \cdot r^2$$

$$= \frac{Wv^2}{2g} + \tfrac{1}{2} I_G \cdot \omega^2 \quad \text{where,} \quad I_G = \sum \frac{W}{g} \cdot r^2 = \frac{W}{g} \cdot k_G^2,$$

the dimension k_G being called the radius of gyration of the link about G.

14.2. Law of Conservation of Energy

This is a statement to the effect that a body, or system of bodies, to which energy is neither added nor extracted, can only have its energy converted from one form to another. For a rigid body having only kinetic and potential energy then,

$$\text{kinetic energy} + \text{potential energy} = \text{constant} \quad (14.2)$$

14.3. Linear Momentum and Impulse

A force applied through the centre of mass of a rigid body, free to move, will cause it to accelerate, i.e. change its velocity, in the direction of the force. The product of the mass and velocity of the body is given the name *momentum*, the rate of change of which is proportional to the applied force.

A force applied to a body for a short period of time, e.g. during an impact, is called an *impulsive force* the effect of which on the body is known as an impulse.

(a) When the impulsive force P acting through the centre of mass of the body is constant over the small period of time t that it is acting, then,

$$\text{impulse} = P \cdot t = \frac{W}{g} \cdot f \cdot t = \frac{W}{g}(v_2 - v_1), \quad \text{where } f \text{ and } v_2 - v_1$$

are the resulting acceleration and velocity changes occurring.

(b) When the impulsive force is variable over the small time period,

$$\text{impulse} = \int_{t_1}^{t_2} P \cdot dt = \int_{v_1}^{v_2} \frac{W}{g} \cdot dv = \frac{W}{g}(v_2 - v_1),$$

and so in both cases (a) and (b), the

$$\text{impulse} = \text{change of linear momentum} \qquad (14.3)$$

14.4. Conservation of Linear Momentum—Linear Impact

When two bodies forming a conservative system collide, the time during which the impact lasts can be considered as a period of mutual compression, and recovery or restitution. The first part of the impact lasts until the bodies are instantaneously moving with the same velocity. Forces may then cause the bodies to separate, i.e. distortion of the bodies may be elastic, or the bodies may exhibit, wholly or in part, some plasticity. Provided the bodies remain in contact the impulsive force of each one on the other must be equal and opposite. Thus the change of linear momentum of each body must be equal and opposite. If, therefore, they are together considered a system, there is no change but a conservation of linear momentum.

In the case of bodies of perfect elasticity, restitution would be equal and opposite to compression, and there would be no loss of energy.

In the case of non- or part-elastic bodies, restitution is not equal to compression, there is a resulting "loss of energy" and plastic bodies will move off together with a common velocity at the end of the compression phase.

The ratio of the impulse of restitution to the impulse of compression is called the coefficient of restitution (e).

WORKED EXAMPLE (U.L.1. EXT. 1948)

14.1. A mass of 600 lb is allowed to fall vertically through 3 ft on to the top of a pile weighing 1000 lb. Assuming that the falling mass and pile remains in contact after impact and that the pile is moved 6 in. at each blow, find, allowing for the action of gravity after impact:

(a) the average resistance against the pile;

(b) the energy lost in the blow.

SOLUTION

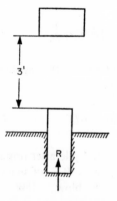

FIG. 14.2. Pile of worked example 14.1

The falling mass, shown in Fig. 14.2, loses potential energy and gains kinetic energy thus:

$$600 \times 3 = \frac{600 \times v_1^2}{2 \times 32 \cdot 2},$$ and the velocity of impact with the pile

$= v_1 = \sqrt{6} \times 32 \cdot 2 = 13 \cdot 88$ ft/sec.

The mass and pile impact, with the change of momentum of the mass equal and opposite to that of the pile and if their common velocity is v, then

$$\frac{600}{32 \cdot 2} (v_1 - v) = \frac{1000}{32 \cdot 2} \times v$$

or

$$v = \frac{600}{1600} \times v_1 = 5 \cdot 2 \text{ ft/sec.}$$

(a) After impact, the mass and the pile have their kinetic energy reduced to zero and lose some potential energy whilst penetrating 6 in. into the ground.

$$\text{K.E. lost} = \frac{1600}{2 \times 32 \cdot 2} \times 5 \cdot 2^2 = 673 \text{ ft lb.}$$

$$\text{P.E. lost} = 1600 \times \frac{6}{12} = 800 \text{ ft lb.}$$

This energy is expended against the resistance of the ground and if R is the average value,

$$R \times \frac{6}{12} = 800 + 673 \quad \text{or} \quad R = \textbf{2946 lb.}$$

(b) The K.E. of mass and pile after impact $= 673$ ft lb.

The K.E. before impact $=$ P.E. of mass $= 600 \times 3$ ft lb.
Hence loss of energy in the blow $= 1800 - 673 = \textbf{1127 ft lb.}$

WORKED EXAMPLE (U.L.1. EXT. 1958)

14.2. A railway truck weighing 12 tons and moving at 8 m.p.h. strikes a stationary truck weighing 15 tons. Determine the velocity (in magnitude and direction) of each truck after separation, assuming no loss of energy at impact.

If each of the four buffers involved in impact has a spring rate of 8 ton/in. compression, find the maximum reaction between the trucks.

SOLUTION

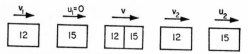

FIG. 14.3. Truck of worked example 14.2

Figure 14.3 shows the trucks before impact, at the instant when both are moving with the same velocity and, after impact. During impact of compression, impulse between trucks is equal and opposite thus,

$$(12 \times 8 - 12 \times v) = 15 \times v$$

or

$$v = \frac{8 \times 12}{27} = 3\tfrac{5}{9} \text{ m.p.h.}$$

Impulse of compression = $12 (8 - 3\tfrac{5}{9})$ or $15 \times 3\tfrac{5}{9}$ units.
Impulse of restitution = $12 (v_1 - 3\tfrac{5}{9})$ or $15 (u_1 - 3\tfrac{5}{9})$ units.
With no loss of energy, these impulses are equal and opposite

$$12 \times 4\tfrac{4}{9} = -12 (v_1 - 3\tfrac{5}{9}) \quad \text{giving} \quad v_1 = -\tfrac{8}{9} \text{ m.p.h.}$$

and

$$u_1 = 2 \times 3\tfrac{5}{9} = 7\tfrac{1}{9} \text{ m.p.h.}$$

After impact has ceased, the 12 ton truck will move *backwards* at $\tfrac{8}{9}$ m.p.h. and the 15 ton truck moves forward at $7\tfrac{1}{9}$ m.p.h. During compression, the buffers have to absorb, as strain energy, any difference between the K.E. of both trucks before impact and when they are together with the common velocity.

$$\text{K.E. before impact} = \frac{12 \times 2240}{64 \cdot 4} \left(\frac{8 \times 44}{30} \right)^2 \text{ ft lb.}$$

K.E. at end of compression $= \dfrac{27 \times 2240}{64 \cdot 4} \left(3\tfrac{5}{9} \times \dfrac{44}{30}\right)^2$ ft lb.

Hence difference of K.E. $= \dfrac{2240}{64 \cdot 4} \times \left(\dfrac{44}{30}\right)^2 \left(12 \times 64 - \dfrac{96^2}{27}\right)$ ft lb

$$= \dfrac{2240}{64 \cdot 4} \times \left(\dfrac{44}{30}\right)^2 \times 427 = 31,900 \text{ ft lb.}$$

If the springs are each compressed *x inches*, then the resistance increases uniformly from 0 to $4 \times 8 \times 2240 \cdot x$ lb and work done = average force × compression

$$= \dfrac{4 \times 8 \times 2240 \cdot x}{2} \; x \text{ in lb}$$

$$= \dfrac{16 \times 2240}{12} \times x^2 \text{ ft lb}$$

and so $\qquad\qquad 16 \times 2240 \times x^2 = 31,900 \times 12$

and $\qquad\qquad x^2 = 10 \cdot 7 \text{ in}^2 \qquad$ or $\qquad x = 3 \cdot 26 \text{ in.}$

Thus spring force $= 3 \cdot 26 \times 2 \times 8 = $ **52 tons** (pair springs/truck)

14.5. Angular Momentum of a Body Rotating about a Fixed Point—Impulsive Torque

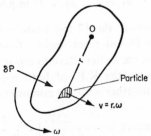

Fig. 14.4. Angular momentum of a link

Figure 14.4 shows a body of weight W rotating at some instant with an angular velocity ω about a fixed point. A particle of weight δW, a distance r from O, will have a velocity $v = r \cdot \omega$ and thus a linear momentum of $(\delta W/g) \cdot r \cdot \omega$.

Let the linear momentum of the particle be changed, over a small interval of time t, by an impulsive force δP, then

$$\delta P \cdot t = \frac{W}{g} \cdot r \cdot \delta \omega \qquad \text{or} \qquad \delta P = \frac{\delta W}{g} \cdot r \cdot \frac{\delta \omega}{t}.$$

Impulsive torque (total) for all particles is

$$T = \frac{\delta \omega}{t} \sum \frac{\delta W}{g} \cdot r^2 = I_0 \cdot \frac{\delta \omega}{t}$$

or

$$T \cdot t = I_0 \cdot \delta \omega = I_0 (\omega_2 - \omega_1). \tag{14.4}$$

The quantity $I_0 \cdot \omega$ is called the angular momentum or moment of momentum of the body about the *fixed* point O. Equation (14.4) shows:

(i) Angular impulse = change of angular momentum.

(ii) The change in angular velocity of a body about a fixed axis

$$= \frac{\text{moment of momentum about the axis}}{\text{moment of inertia about the axis}}.$$

WORKED EXAMPLE (U.L.1. EXT. 1952)

14.3. Figure 14.5 shows a tilt hammer, hinged at O with its head A resting on top of the pile B. The hammer, including the arm OA, weighs 56 lb. Its centre of gravity G is 16 in. horizontally from O, and its radius of gyration about an axis through G parallel to the axis of the pin O is 3 in. The pile weighs 300 lb.

The hammer is raised through 45° to the position shown in dotted lines, and released. On striking the pile there is no rebound. Find the angular velocity of the hammer immediately before impact and the linear velocity of the pile immediately after impact. Neglect any impulsive resistance offered by the earth into which the pile is driven.

SOLUTION

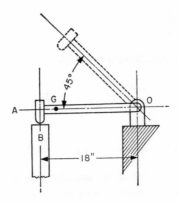

FIG. 14.5. Tilt hammer of worked example 14.3

Whilst the hammer and arm swings about O, the loss of P.E. = gain in angular K.E., and from Fig. 14.5,

$$\text{Loss of P.E.} = 56 \times \frac{16 \cdot \cos 45^\circ}{12} = 52 \cdot 8 \text{ ft lb.}$$

Moment of inertia of hammer and arm about $O = I_0$

$$= \frac{W}{g}(k_G^2 + x^2) = \frac{56}{32 \cdot 2} \times \left(\frac{3}{12}\right)^2 + \frac{56}{32 \cdot 2} \times \left(\frac{16}{12}\right)^2 \text{ slugs ft}^2$$

$$= 3 \cdot 2 \text{ slugs ft}^2.$$

Thus $52 \cdot 8 = \frac{1}{2} \times 3 \cdot 2 \times \omega^2$ and so $\omega^2 = 33$, $\omega = \mathbf{5 \cdot 74 \text{ rad/sec}}$

For the impact, angular momentum of hammer and pile about O before impact, $= I_0 \cdot \omega$, since that of pile $= 0$.

Angular momentum of hammer and pile about O after impact

$$= I_0 \cdot \omega_1 + \frac{W_1}{g} \cdot v_1 \cdot \frac{18}{12}$$

if ω_1 and v_1 are the velocities of hammer and pile respectively. Thus

$$3 \cdot 2 \times 5 \cdot 74 = 3 \cdot 2\omega_1 + \frac{300}{32 \cdot 2} \times v_1 \times \frac{18}{12}. \quad \text{But } v_1 = \frac{18}{12} \cdot \omega_1$$

and so

$$3 \cdot 2 \times 5 \cdot 74 = 3 \cdot 2\omega_1 + \frac{300}{32 \cdot 2} \times \left(\frac{18}{12}\right)^2 \cdot \omega_1$$

$$\omega_1 = \frac{5 \cdot 7}{7 \cdot 53} \text{ rad/sec}$$

and thus
$$v_1 = \frac{5 \cdot 7 \times 18}{7 \cdot 53 \times 12} = \textbf{1·14 ft/sec.}$$

WORKED EXAMPLE (U.L.1. EXT. 1941)

14.4. Two gear wheels A and B are mounted on parallel shafts so that they may revolve separately or may be meshed together externally. The wheels were originally turning freely in the same direction.

Wheel	Mass (lb)	Number of teeth	Radius of gyration (in.)	Original rev/min
A	10	100	12	300
B	12	50	10	100

Find (a) the speed and direction of rotation of wheel A, if the gears are suddenly meshed, assuming there is no backlash of the teeth, (b) the loss of energy in ft lb due to impact.

SOLUTION

(a) Change of angular velocity of A = angular momentum about axis of A × moment of inertia about axis of A

$$_2\omega_A - {}_1\omega_A = \frac{P \cdot r_A \cdot t}{I_A} \tag{14.5}$$

and similarly $\quad _2\omega_B - {}_1\omega_B = \dfrac{P \cdot r_B \cdot t}{I_B}$

$$\tag{14.6}$$

the symbols having the meanings of section 14.5.

Note that care must be taken not to assume that when two bodies rotate about *different* centres, the changes of angular momenta are the same, i.e. do not "parrot cry" momentum before = momentum after.

Taking the ratio of equations (14.5) and (14.6), gives

$$\frac{_2\omega_A - {}_1\omega_A}{_2\omega_B - {}_1\omega_B} = \frac{r_A \cdot I_B}{r_B \cdot I_A} = \frac{I_B}{I_A} \times \frac{\text{teeth on } A}{\text{teeth on } B}.$$

However, due to the meshing, $_2\omega_B = -\,_2\omega_A \cdot \dfrac{r_A}{r_B}$.

Thus

$$\frac{_2\omega_A - 300}{-\,_2\omega_A \times 2 - 100} = \frac{12 \times 10^2 \times 100}{10 \times 12^2 \times 50} = \frac{5}{3}$$

(common factors g, 2π, 60, etc., cancelling)

$$3 \times {}_2\omega_A - 900 = -10\,{}_2\omega_A - 500$$

$$_2\omega_A = +\,\mathbf{30 \cdot 77\ rev/min}\ \text{(i.e. in same direction)}$$

and

$$_2\omega_B = - \ 61\cdot54 \ \textbf{rev/min} \ \text{(i.e. in opposite direction).}$$

(b) Initial K.E. of wheels A and B

$$= \tfrac{1}{2}\left\{ \frac{10}{32\cdot2} \times \left(\frac{12}{12}\right)^2 \left(\frac{300}{60} \times 2\pi\right)^2 + \frac{12}{32\cdot2} \times \left(\frac{10}{12}\right)^2 \left(\frac{100}{60} \times 2\pi\right)^2 \right\}$$

$$= 167\cdot2 \ \text{ft lb.}$$

Final K.E. of wheels A and B

$$= \tfrac{1}{2}\left\{ \frac{10}{32\cdot2} \times \left(\frac{12}{12}\right)^2 \left(\frac{30\cdot77}{60} \times 2\pi\right)^2 + \frac{12}{32\cdot2} \times \left(\frac{10}{12}\right)^2 \left(\frac{61\cdot54}{60} + 2\pi\right)^2 \right\}$$

$$= 6\cdot53 \ \text{ft lb.}$$

Loss of K.E. due to impact $= 167\cdot2 - 6\cdot53 = \textbf{160·7 ft lb.}$

WORKED EXAMPLE (U.L.2. EXT. 1951)

14.5. A 2 ft square downward opening trap door has a horizontal frictionless pin joint along one edge. The door weighs 12 lb, has its centre of gravity at its centre of symmetry, has its weight uniformly distributed, and, when closed, lies in a horizontal plane. When the catch is released, the door accelerates downwards about the horizontal pin joint, until it finally hangs vertical. At this instant the centre of the lower edge of the door comes in contact with a horizontal coil spring of stiffness 100 lb/in., which acts as a buffer, absorbing the kinetic energy of the door by compression. The angle through which the door turns beyond the vertical position in compressing the spring is small.

If the door catch is suddenly released when the door is in the closed position, determine:

(i) the instantaneous acceleration of the centre of gravity of the door at the moment of release;

(ii) the instantaneous force on the pin at the moment of release;
(iii) the maximum compression of the horizontal spring;
(iv) the horizontal force on the pin joint at the moment of
maximum compression of the spring.

SOLUTION

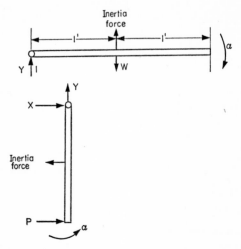

FIG. 14.6. Forces on door of worked example 14.5

(i) Torque acting on door at moment of release $= W \times 1$ lb ft.
Hence, from $T = I \cdot a$,

$$a = \frac{W \times 1}{(W/g) \cdot (2/3^2)} = \frac{3 \cdot g}{4} = 24 \cdot 15 \text{ rad/sec}^2.$$

(ii) Figure 14·6 shows the forces acting at moment of release
and for dynamic equilibrium they are; weight of door, inertia
force and some vertical force Y, at the hinge.

$$\text{Inertia force} = \frac{W}{g} \cdot f = \frac{W}{g} \cdot l \cdot a = \frac{3 \cdot W}{4} \text{ lb upwards.}$$

Thus in vertical direction,

$$Y + \text{inertia force} = \text{weight of door}$$

$$Y = W - \frac{3 \times W}{4} = \frac{W}{4} = \textbf{3 lb.}$$

(iii) When the door has compressed the spring the maximum amount, the loss of potential energy of door = gain in strain energy of the spring. If spring compression is δ and P the maximum force

$$W \times 1 = \tfrac{1}{2}P \,.\, \delta = \tfrac{1}{2}S \,.\, \delta^2$$

hence
$$\delta = \sqrt{\frac{2 \times W}{S}} = \sqrt{\frac{2 \times 12}{100 \times 12}} \text{ ft} = 0{\cdot}142 \text{ ft}$$

or
$$\textbf{1·7 in.}$$

(iv) Figure 14.6 shows the door in vertical position with the forces acting. Impulsive force P is due to spring $= 100 \times 1{\cdot}7 = 170$ lb.

$$a = \frac{170 \times 2}{(12/32{\cdot}2) \times (4/3)} = \frac{170 \times 2 \times 32{\cdot}2 \times 3}{12 \times 4} = 684 \text{ rad/sec}^2$$

and so

$$f = 684 \text{ ft/sec}^2 \text{ and inertia force} = \frac{12 \times 684}{32{\cdot}2} = 255 \text{ lb.}$$

If X and Y are horizontal and vertical components of the hinge reaction due to impulsive force,

$$X + 170 = 255 \qquad \text{giving} \qquad X = \textbf{85 lb.}$$

Note (i) $Y =$ weight of door since there is no centrifugal force in this position.

K*

(ii) It is possible for the inertia force to equal the impulsive force and then there is no component force on the hinge in their directions. The point of application of the impulsive force is then called the *centre of percussion*.

14.6. Equivalent Inertia of a Simple Gear Train

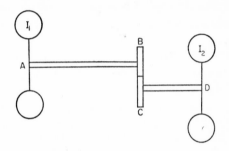

Fig. 14.7. Simple gear train

Figure 14.7 shows a simple gear train in which a shaft carrying a rotor of inertia I_1, at A, is connected at B and C by a simple gear drive to another shaft carrying a rotor of inertia I_2, at D. The torque required at A to accelerate the train is required, assuming the inertia of the gears themselves are ignored. Let the angular acceleration of shaft CD be a_2 then torque to accelerate $CD = I_2 . a_2$.

Torque on gear B to accelerate CD

$$= \frac{\text{torque on } CD}{\text{pitch circle radius of gear } C} \times \text{pitch circle radius of } B$$

$$= I_2 . a_2 \times \frac{\text{speed of shaft } CD}{\text{speed of shaft } AB} = I_2 . a_2/G$$

where G is the gear speed ratio of B to C.

But the angular acceleration of $AB = G \times$ angular acceleration of CD, hence

$$a_1 = a_2 \cdot G.$$

Thus torque on AB to accelerate $CD = \dfrac{I_2 \cdot a_1}{G^2}.$

Torque on AB to accelerate $AB = I_1 \cdot a_1$.
Total torque on AB to accelerate the train $ABCD$

$$= I_1 \cdot a_1 + I_2 \cdot a_1/G^2$$

$$= a_1 (I_1 + I_2/G^2) = a_1 \cdot I_E. \tag{14.7}$$

Thus the train is equivalent to a rotor of inertia I_E where $I_E = I_1 + I_2/G^2$ having an acceleration a_1.

This analysis can be similarly extended for several shafts geared together to give $I_E = I_1 + I_N/G_N^2$, but the result is of little value to examination candidates who are advised to consider problems basically.

Worked Examples (U.L.1. Ext. 1948)

14.6. The engine of a motor-car runs at 3420 rev/min when the road speed is 60 m.p.h. The weight of the car is 2400 lb. The inertia of the rotating parts of the engine corresponds to 24 lb at a radius of gyration of 0·48 ft, and that of the road wheels to 240 lb at 0·8 ft. The efficiency of the transmission is 0·9 and the wind resistance is 200 lb. The road wheel diameter is 2·5 ft. Estimate the horsepower developed by the engine when the car travels on a level road at 60 m.p.h. with an acceleration of 3 ft/sec².

Solution

Angular velocity of wheels at 60 m.p.h.

$$= \frac{60 \times 44}{30} \times \frac{1}{1 \cdot 25} = 70 \cdot 3 \text{ rad/sec.}$$

Angular velocity of engine $= \dfrac{3420}{60} \times 2\pi = 358$ rad/sec.

Hence gear ratio $= \dfrac{358}{70\cdot3} = 5\cdot08$.

Working from the wheel conditions through the gear drive to the engine, the various torques are evaluated and the required engine torque obtained.

Force at road wheels to give car its linear acceleration

$$= W \cdot f/g = \frac{2400 \times 3}{32\cdot2} = 223\cdot5 \text{ lb.}$$

Force for linear acceleration and to overcome wind resistance

$$= 223\cdot5 + 200 = 423\cdot5 \text{ lb.}$$

Torque at wheels for this $= 423\cdot5 \times$ wheel radius

$$= 423\cdot5 \times 1\cdot25 = 530 \text{ lb ft.}$$

Acceleration of wheels $a_w = f/r = 3/1\cdot25 = 2\cdot4$ rad/sec^2.
Torque on wheels to accelerate wheels $= I_w a_w$

$$= \frac{240}{32\cdot2} \times 0\cdot8^2 \times 2\cdot4$$

$$= 11\cdot4 \text{ lb ft.}$$

Total torque supplied to the wheels $= 530 + 11\cdot4 = 541\cdot4$ lb ft.
Torque from engine for this (if 100% efficiency)

$$= \frac{541\cdot4}{\text{gear ratio}} = \frac{541\cdot4}{5\cdot08} = 106 \text{ lb ft.}$$

Torque from engine (90% efficiency) $= \dfrac{106}{0\cdot9} = 118$ lb ft.

Acceleration of engine $= 2\cdot4 \times 5\cdot08 = 12\cdot2$ rad/sec^2.

Torque to accelerate engine parts $= I_e a_e = \dfrac{24}{32 \cdot 2} \times 0 \cdot 48^2 \times 12 \cdot 2$

$$= 2 \cdot 09 \text{ lb ft.}$$

Total torque required to be developed by engine $= 118 + 2 \cdot 09$

$$= 120 \cdot 1 \text{ lb ft (approx.).}$$

Engine power $= \dfrac{2\pi \times 3420 \times 120 \cdot 1}{33,000} = \textbf{78·4 h.p.}$

Worked Example (U.L.2. Ext. 1951)

14.7. A motor vehicle weighs 2000 lb and has road wheels of 24 in. rolling diameter. The total moment of inertia of all four road wheels together with half shafts is 200 lb ft², while that of the engine and clutch is 20 lb ft². The engine torque is 100 lb ft, the transmission efficiency is 90 per cent and the tractive resistance is constant at 100 lb. Determine (a) the gear ratio between engine and road wheels to give maximum acceleration on an upgrade of 1 in 20, and (b) this acceleration in ft/sec².

Solution

(a) Let the required gear ratio be G and linear acceleration f ft/sec².

Tractive force required from wheels

$$= \underset{\substack{\text{tractive} \\ \text{resistance}}}{100} + \underset{\text{gradient}}{\dfrac{2000}{20}} + \underset{\substack{\text{linear} \\ \text{acceleration}}}{\dfrac{2000 \cdot f}{32 \cdot 2}} \text{ lb.}$$

Torque from wheels for this $= (200 + 62 \cdot 2f)\dfrac{12}{12}$

$$= 200 + 62 \cdot 2f \text{ lb ft.}$$

Inertia torque of wheels $= \dfrac{200}{32 \cdot 2} \times \dfrac{12}{12} \cdot f = 6 \cdot 2f$ lb ft.

Hence total torque to wheels $= 200 + 68 \cdot 4f$ lb ft.

Torque from engine for wheels, etc., $= \left[\dfrac{200 + 68 \cdot 4f}{G} \right] \times \dfrac{100}{90}$ lb ft.

Inertia torque for engine $= \dfrac{20}{32 \cdot 2} \times G \times .f = 0 \cdot 62\,G\, . f$ lb ft.

Hence torque needed to be developed by engine

$$= 100 = \left(\frac{200 + 68 \cdot 4f}{G} \right) \frac{100}{90} + 0 \cdot 62\,G\,.f$$

giving

$$f = \frac{900G - 2000}{5 \cdot 58G^2 + 684} \text{ ft/sec}^2, \quad \text{and for } G \text{ to be a maximum,}$$

$$\mathrm{d}f/\mathrm{d}G = 0 = \frac{900\,(5 \cdot 58G^2 + 684) - 11 \cdot 16G\,(900G - 2000)}{(5 \cdot 58G^2 + 684)^2}$$

whence $G^2 - 4 \cdot 44G - 122 = 0$, the positive root giving $G = \mathbf{13 \cdot 5}$.

(b)
$$f = \frac{900 \times 13 \cdot 5 - 2000}{5 \cdot 58 \times 13 \cdot 5^2 + 684} = \mathbf{5 \cdot 97 \text{ ft sec}^2.}$$

WORKED EXAMPLE (U.L.2. EXT. 1955)

14.8. A vehicle having a wheel base of 11 ft. is driven along a horizontal road by a torque applied to the rear wheels. The centre of gravity is 2·5 ft above the ground and 4·5 ft behind the front axle. The coefficient of friction between the wheels and ground is 0·3. Determine:

(a) the maximum acceleration of the vehicle if the wheels are not to slip;

(b) the maximum retardation of the vehicle when a braking torque is applied to the rear wheels.

SOLUTION

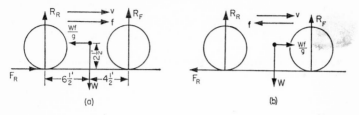

FIG. 14.8. Forces on vehicle of worked example 14.7

(a) Figure 14.8a shows the forces acting.

Horizontal forces give $F_R = W \cdot f/g = \mu \cdot R_R$ for maximum traction. Moments of forces about point of contact of front wheels and road give,

$$R_R \times 11 = \frac{W}{g} \cdot f \times 2 \cdot 5 + W \times 4 \cdot 5$$

$$R_R = \frac{W \cdot f}{g} \times \frac{2 \cdot 5}{11} + W \times \frac{4 \cdot 5}{11}.$$

Hence

$$\frac{W \cdot f}{g} \times \frac{2 \cdot 5 \times 0 \cdot 3}{11} + \frac{W \times 4 \cdot 5 \times 0 \cdot 3}{11} = \frac{W \cdot f}{g}$$

and so

$$f(1 - 0 \cdot 0628) = \frac{4 \cdot 5 \times 0 \cdot 3 \times 32 \cdot 2}{11}$$

$$f = \mathbf{4 \cdot 24 \ ft/sec^2}.$$

(b) Figure 14.8b shows the forces acting. Note that the frictional forces oppose motion and inertia force.

Horizontal forces give

$$F_R = \frac{W \cdot f}{g} = \mu \cdot R_R \quad \text{for maximum braking.}$$

Moments about point of contact of front wheels with road,

$$\frac{W \cdot f}{g} \times 2{\cdot}5 + R_R \times 11 = W \times 4{\cdot}5$$

whence, by the method of part (a), $f = \mathbf{3{\cdot}7}$ **ft/sec²**.

Examples

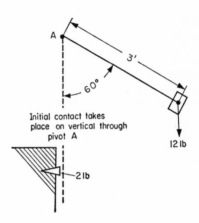

Initial contact takes
place on vertical through
pivot A

2 lb

12 lb

FIG. 14.9. Hammer of example 14.9

14.9. Figure 14.9 shows a hammer weighing 12 lb and pivoted at A. It falls against a wedge weighing 2 lb which is driven forwards ¼ in., by the impact, into a heavy rigid block. The resistance to the wedge varies uniformly with the distance through which it moves, varying from zero to R lb.

Neglecting the small amount by which the hammer rises after passing through the vertical through A and assuming that the hammer does not rebound, find

(a) the value of R;

(b) the time interval during which the wedge is moving forward.

Answer: (a) 1495 lb; (b) 0·00386 sec.   (U.L.1. Ext. 1945)

14.10. A railway truck weighing 16 tons while travelling at 4 m.p.h. strikes another truck weighing 12 tons and travelling at 1 m.p.h. in the same direction.

   (a) Find their common speed as they come together and the final speed of each assuming that the buffers act normally and neglecting all friction.

   (b) If the total stiffness of the buffer springs is 6 ton/in. compression and the springs can only be compressed 5 in., what will be the final speed referred to in (a) above?

Answer: (a) $2\frac{5}{7}$, $4\frac{3}{7}$, $1\frac{3}{7}$ m.p.h.; (b) no change.   (U.L.2. Ext. 1955)

14.11. Two coaxial shafts A and B are connected by a friction clutch which at first is disengaged. On A there is a flywheel weighing 200 lb of radius of gyration 18 in. rotating at 100 rev/min. On B there are rotating parts weighing 500 lb of radius of gyration 25 in. rotating in the same direction as A at 20 rev/min. The clutch is now let into engagement and after 3 sec the two shafts are rotating with the same angular velocity. Find this angular velocity and the loss of kinetic energy. Assuming that the torque transmitted by the clutch during the 3 sec is constant, find its magnitude. Find also the angle in radians through which one face of the clutch slips relative to the other face.

Answer: 33·8 rev/min, 403·5 ft lb, 32·8 lb ft, 12·3 rad.   (U.L.1. Ext. 1950)

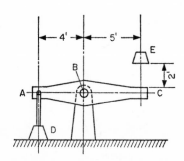

FIG. 14.10. Beam of example 14.12

14.12. The beam ABC, shown in Fig. 14.10, is free to rotate about the shaft B. The weight of the beam is 50 lb, its C.G. is at B, and its radius of gyration about the shaft B is 3 ft. The weight D, 10 lb, rests on the floor. A weight E, of 6 lb, falls 2 ft, and strikes the beam without rebounding. Find how far D is lifted.

Answer: 0·947 ft.   (U.L.2. Ext. 1950)

14.13. Define the "centre of percussion" of a compound pendulum, and proving any formula used, show how its position may be calculated, given the distance from the axis of supension to the centre of gravity and the radius of gyration about the axis of suspension.

A uniform baulk of timber 12 ft long weighing 700 lb can swing in a vertical plane about knife edges fitted 2 ft below its upper end. Initially, the baulk is vertical and at rest. A bullet weighing $\frac{1}{2}$ lb strikes the baulk normally at its centre of percussion, and causes the lower end of the baulk to swing 18 in. to one side. The bullet remains in the baulk. Find the velocity of the bullet immediately before striking the baulk.

Answer: 1810 ft/sec.   (U.L.2. Ext. 1952)

14.14. The tailboard of a lorry is 5 ft long and 2·5 ft high. It is hinged along the bottom edge to the floor of the lorry. Chains are attached to the top corners of the board and to the sides of the lorry so that when the board is in a horizontal position the chains are parallel and inclined at 45° to the horizontal. A tension spring is inserted in each chain so as to reduce the shock and these are adjusted to prevent the board from dropping below the horizontal. Each spring exerts a force of 300 lb/in. of extension.

Find the greatest force in each spring and the resultant force at the hinges when the board falls freely from the vertical position. Assume that the tailboard is a uniform body weighing 60 lb.

Answer: 520 lb, 829 lb.   (U.L.2. Ext. 1946)

14.15. A car weighing 3000 lb has, when running on the level, a resistance to motion of $a + bV^2$ lb, where a is 60 lb, b is a constant and V the speed in m.p.h. It is also found that the car maintains a speed of 80 m.p.h. with an effective horsepower of 50 when running on the level. Find:

(i) the value of b,

(ii) how far the car will run up a slope of 1 in 10 before the speed drops to 40 m.p.h. assuming it starts at 80 m.p.h. and that a constant torque is maintained.

Answer: (i) 0·0272; (ii) 2100 ft.   (U.L.1. Ext. 1954)

14.16. A motor car weighs 3000 lb. The wheels, axles, etc, running at road wheel speed weigh 540 lb. with a radius of gyration of 8 in. The engine and gear parts running at engine speed weigh 192 lb with a radius of gyration of 3 in. The effective wheel diameter is 27 in., the engine torque is 90 lb ft, the transmission efficient is 84 per cent and the road resistance is 80 lb. Under these conditions calculate the acceleration of the car in ft/sec²:

  (a) in top gear ratio, engine speed/wheel speed = 5,

  (b) in bottom gear, engine speed/wheel speed = 16.

Answer: 2·44 ft/sec²; (b) 6·12 ft/sec². (A.M.I.Mech.E. 1950)

14.17. A motor vehicle, total weight 3000 lb, has road wheels of 24 in. diameter. The effective moment of inertia of the four road wheels and rear axles together is 160 lb ft², while that of the engine and flywheel is 20 lb ft². The transmission efficiency is 85 per cent and the tractive resistance at a speed of 15 m.p.h. is 60 lb. The total torque available is 150 lb ft.

  (a) Determine the gear ratio, engine to back axle, to provide maximum acceleration on an upgrade whose sine is 0·25, when travelling at 15 m.p.h.

  (b) What is this maximum acceleration?

  (c) Determine the engine rev/min and horsepower under these conditions. (U.L.2. Ext. 1953)

Answer: (a) 21·3; (b) 5·66 ft/sec²; (c) 4500 rev/min, 128 h.p.

14.18. A car travelling down an incline of 1 in 13 at 20 m.p.h. experiences a frictional resistance to motion of 70 lb in addition to a frictional torque on the engine of 0·0012N lb ft, when N is the engine speed in rev/min. The total weight of the car is 3000 lb. The wheels are 26 in. diameter and have a total moment of inertia of 75 lb ft². The engine torque is 50 lb ft. The rotating parts of the engine and flywheel have a moment of inertia of 10 lb ft². There is a four-speed gearbox, giving ratios of 20, 13, 8 and 5 between the engine speed and the axle speed. What gear ratio should be selected for maximum acceleration? How much will the acceleration be?

Answer: 13, 5·12 ft/sec². (U.L.2. Ext. 1946)

14.19. A motor car weighing 2500 lb has axles 8 ft apart. When standing on a level road, the centre of gravity of the car is 2 ft above ground level and 3 ft in front of the rear axle. Calculate the normal reaction on each wheel when the car is moving down a gradient of 1 in 20 against a wind pressure of 40 lb acting parallel to the road and 2 ft 6 in. from it, with the engine switched off and the rear brakes applied so as to give a deceleration of 2 ft/sec². What must the coefficient of friction between the rear wheels and the road be if the rear wheels are not to skid under these conditions?

(U.L.1. Ext. 1950)

Answer: 752·5 lb each rear wheel, 497·5 lb each front wheel, 0·157.

14.20. A motor vehicle has a wheel base of 8 ft and centre of gravity 3 ft behind the front axle and 2 ft above the ground. The vehicle is allowed to run freely down an incline whose sine is ⅛, until a speed of 30 m.p.h. is attained. The hand brake is then fully applied so as to provide the maximum possible braking effect on the rear wheels only. If μ between tyres and road surface is 0·4 calculate the speed of the vehicle after a distance of 200 ft from rest has been covered. Comment on your answer.

Answer: 30·3 m.p.h. (still accelerating).　　　　　　　　　(U.L.1. Ext. 1956)

CHAPTER FIFTEEN

LUBRICATION

It is well known that the frictional drag between two contacting metal surfaces, when moved relative to one another, can be considerably reduced by the presence of a lubricant. The viscosity and oiliness of the lubricant, together with other physical properties, play an important part in the lubrication which now is generally recognised as either boundary or film.

15.1. Boundary Lubrication

Under boundary conditions lubrication is by oily contamination or closely adherent films of oil only a few molecules thick. The roughness of the contacting surfaces is, therefore, still significant and frictional drag is still largely conditioned by the so-called dry friction. Resistance is due, to a marked extent, to the shearing of surface irregularities or to their plastic deformation. However, the molecules of the lubricant form a chemical bond with those of the metal surface, which is much stronger than that between adjacent lubricant molecules, i.e. a layer of molecules is said to be adsorbed by the metal. Some characteristics of boundary lubrication may be explained by assuming that the presence of the absorbed layer reduces the amount of plastic deformation of the metal surfaces whilst still adhering. There is a consequent lowering of the coefficient of friction whilst the frictional drag keeps its dry friction character.

Considerable attention is still being given to boundary conditions since this type of lubrication commonly occurs, particularly in critical conditions in engineering. However, no rigid theory, generally acceptable, is yet available to explain certain known phenomena, and design is often made on the basis of boundary conditions representing a limiting case of film lubrication.

15.2. Film Lubrication—Viscosity

This is theoretically the ideal form of lubrication in which the two metal surfaces are completely separated by a film of lubricant. Relative motion of a metal surface across a fluid is accompanied by a tangential drag of the metal surface on the fluid and, subsequently, between the layers of the fluid itself. The lubricant is sheared at the layer planes and this shearing is resisted by the property of the lubricant called viscosity.

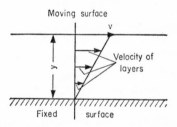

FIG. 15.1. Viscous drag on a flat surface

Figure 15.1 shows a surface moving relatively across a lubricant and separated from another surface by a film of lubricant of thickness y. The lower surface is assumed to be at rest and the upper surface to be moving with velocity v. Layers of the lubricant will be sheared, and it is assumed that there is a constant rate of shearing across the film given by v/y, ft/sec/ft. If the shearing force across any layer is F and the surface area of shear is A, then the shearing stress is F/A lb/ft². The viscosity is then defined as the ratio of the shear stress to the rate of shear and is found to be constant for some fluids called Newtonian fluids. Thus, the coefficient of viscosity,

$$\eta = \frac{\text{viscous shear stress}}{\text{rate of shear}} = \frac{F/A}{v/y}. \tag{15.1}$$

The units of viscosity can be expressed in terms of the basic quantities of mass M, length L and time T.

$$\text{Stress} = \frac{\text{force}}{\text{area}} = \text{mass} \times \frac{\text{acceleration}}{\text{area}} = \frac{M \cdot L/T^2}{L^2} = \frac{M}{L \cdot T^2}$$

$$\text{Rate of shear} = \frac{\text{velocity}}{\text{distance}} = \frac{L/T}{L} = \frac{1}{T}$$

Thus,
$$\text{viscosity} = \frac{M}{L \cdot T^2} \div \frac{1}{T} = \frac{M}{L \cdot T}$$

In the C.G.S. system, one unit is called a *Poise*, i.e. 1 gm per cm sec.

In the British and American system, one unit is 1 slug per ft sec, for which there is no name, but one unit = 478 poise; or alternatively, 1 lb mass per ft sec = 14·88 poise.

15.3. Film Lubrication of Flat Surfaces

The lubricant film which separates the surfaces has, in addition to resisting shear, to support the load carried between the two surfaces.

Figure 15.2 shows the surfaces of Fig. 15.1, slightly tilted to form a wedge-shaped section. If it is assumed that there is no leakage of lubricant in a transverse direction, then all of it must flow in the tangential direction and a continuous flow is required. The film thickness varies and so, for continuity of flow in the direction of slip, the velocity must also vary. At any section there

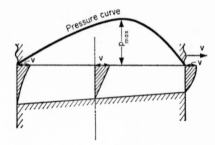

FIG. 15.2. Pressure distribution between two flat surfaces

is, therefore, a gradation of velocity along the film as well as across it. The shaded area shows the variation and each curve is such that the areas shown are equal. Corresponding to these velocities are film pressures, with values in the direction of flow varying from atmospheric at the ends to some maximum, as shown in Fig. 15.2. The resultant effect of this pressure on the moving surface is to support the load carried, the tilting of the surfaces aiding the generation of a film.

15.4. Film Lubrication in a Journal Bearing

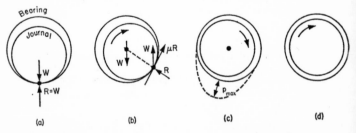

FIG. 15.3. Positions taken up by rotating journal

Figure 15.3a, shows a journal carried by a bearing whose diameter is slightly larger than that of the journal. When at rest the contact between journal and bearing is at the lowest point and the reaction, R, of the bearing on the journal $= W$, the load carried by the journal.

When the journal is rotated slowly, the contact point moves, as shown in Fig. 15.3b, so that the resultant of the normal reaction and boundary friction drag μ . R equals the load carried by the journal.

When the speed is increased, the viscous drag is sufficient to make the fluid flow past the contact point, and the wedge effect of the converging space between journal and bearing is sufficient for film lubrication to be set up. The shaft then assumes the position shown in Fig. 15.3c, the fluid pressure having a maximum value in the position indicated.

When the journal speed is high enough to develop a film, and the *load carried* by it *small*, it occupies an approximately concentric position shown in Fig. 15.3d. The frictional drag is then solely due to the viscous shear of the film.

15.5. Effective Coefficient of Friction of a Journal Bearing

The frictional torque in a journal bearing may be expressed as $T = \mu$. W . r, where W is the load carried by the bearing, r its

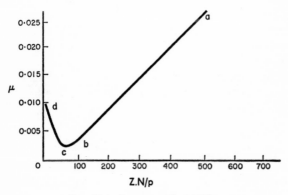

Fig. 15.4. Curve μ against ZN/p

radius and μ some effective coefficient of friction. The coefficient μ is dependent upon the viscosity Z of the lubricant, the speed of rotation N of the journal and the bearing pressure p given by the load W per projected bearing area.

The coefficient μ is related to these physical quantities, in the dimensionless group $Z \cdot N/p$, by the curve of Fig. 15.4.

The region ab is one of film lubrication, bc a transitional region and cd a region of boundary lubrication.

WORKED EXAMPLE (A.M.I.Mech.E. 1956)

15.1. Define "poise" and "stoke" and give units. A 4 in. diameter journal rotates concentrically in a bush of diameter 4·01 in. and length 8 in. The annular space between bush and journal is filled with oil, S.G. 0·86. If it takes 10 h.p. to overcome viscous resistance of the oil at 2400 rev/min., find the absolute and kinematic viscosities of the oil, expressing the values in metric units.

SOLUTION

The journal and bush represents a concentric system described in section 15.4 and shown in Fig. 15.3d. Velocity of shaft at periphery $= (2400/60) \times 2\pi \times 2 = 503$ in/sec. Thickness of oil film $= 0·005$ in. and so velocity gradient $= 503/0·005 = 100,600$ in/sec/in. or ft/sec/ft.

Torque on shaft $= 10 \times 33,000/2\pi \times 2400 = 21·9$ lb ft or 262·8 lb in.

Tangential shearing force at 2 in. radius $= 262·8/2 = 131·4$ lb acting on a cylindrical surface area of $2\pi \times 2 \times 8 = 32\pi$ in^2.

Hence, shear stress $= 131·4/32\pi = 1·31$ lb/in^2 or, 189 lb/ft^2.

$$\text{Viscosity} = \frac{\text{shear stress}}{\text{rate of shear}} = \frac{189}{100,600} \text{ slug/ft sec}$$

$$= \frac{189 \times 478}{100,600} = \textbf{0·90 poise.}$$

Kinematic viscosity $= \dfrac{\text{absolute viscosity}}{\text{density}} = \dfrac{0.90}{0.86} = \mathbf{1 \cdot 05 \text{ stokes.}}$

WORKED EXAMPLE

15.2. A vertical shaft of 3 in. diameter rests in a footstool bearing and rotates at 750 rev/min. If the end of the shaft and the surface of the bearing are perfectly flat and assumed to be separated by a film of oil 0·001 in. thick, find the torque required to rotate the shaft, and the power absorbed in overcoming the viscous resistance of the oil film. The coefficient of viscosity of the oil is $\eta = 40$ centipoise.

SOLUTION

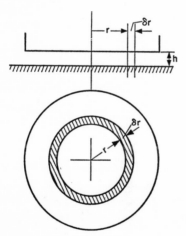

FIG. 15.5. Bearing of worked example 15.2

Consider, as shown in Fig. 15.5, an elementary ring of surface radius r and width δr.

Circumferential velocity at radius $r = \omega \,.\, r$ and if the film has thickness h, the velocity gradient $= \omega \,.\, r/h$

$$= \frac{750}{60} \times 2\pi \times \frac{r}{0 \cdot 001} \text{ in/sec/in. or ft/sec/ft if } r \text{ is in inches.}$$

Shear stress $= \eta \times$ velocity gradient

$$\frac{0 \cdot 40}{478} \times \frac{750}{60} \times \frac{2\pi \times r}{0 \cdot 001} = 65 \cdot 6r \text{ lb/ft}^2.$$

Shear force $\dfrac{65 \cdot 6r}{144} \times 2\pi \cdot r \cdot \delta r$ lb.

Torque $= \dfrac{65 \cdot 6r}{144} \times 2\pi \times r^2 \cdot \delta r$ lb in. $= 2 \cdot 86r^3 \cdot \delta r$ lb in.

Total torque $= \displaystyle\int_0^{1 \cdot 5} 2 \cdot 86r^3 \mathrm{d}r$ lb in. $= \dfrac{2 \cdot 86 \times 1 \cdot 5^4}{4}$

$$= \textbf{3·62 lb in.}$$

Power absorbed $= \dfrac{2\pi \times 750 \times 3 \cdot 62}{33{,}000 \times 12} = \textbf{0·043 h.p.}$